GIFT AID

Home—An Anthology of Modern Irish Writing

FOCUS POINT IRELAND

WOULD LIKE TO THANK

IRISH PERMANENT PLC

FOR GENEROUSLY SUPPORTING

THE PUBLICATION

OF THIS BOOK

Home—An Anthology of Modern Irish Writing

Edited by

Siobhán Parkinson

A. & A. Farmar

© The Selection Focus Point Ireland 1996
The acknowledgements on pp xi–xiii consitute an extension
of this copyright declaration.

British Library Cataloguing in Publication Data
A CIP catalogue record for this book is available from the British Library

Cover illustration by Martin Gale
Cover and text design by Dunbar Design
Typesetting by A. & A. Farmar
Printed by Betaprint

ISBN 0 899047 24 7

A. & A. Farmar
Beech House
78 Ranelagh Village
Dublin 6
Ireland

CONTENTS

PART 3

The Lost Citadel

PART 4

Striding the Paths of This Parish

Preface

The writers whose work appears in this wonderful anthology responded with great generosity to Focus Point Ireland's invitation to contribute a piece of writing, published or unpublished, on the theme of 'home'.

Some reflected on their childhood homes, laden with memories of house and family, not all happy memories, but deeply personal and rooted in place. These we have gathered in the first part, 'The House Remembered'. Many of these pieces give expression to the Focus philosophy of the meaning of home, as do those in Part 2, 'Built on our Embrace', which is about new homes, sometimes that of a couple starting out together.

Part 3, 'The Lost Citadel', is concerned with loss and displacement, the breaking up of homes, and much of the writing has an undertow of despair, an atmosphere familiar to those of us who have experienced homelessness or who work with people who are or have been out-of-home. And finally, 'Striding the Paths of this Parish' is about homecomings, events that for many people, including the writers in this section, seem to be a curious mixture of joy and regret.

As a national agency concerned with housing and homelessness, Focus Point Ireland believes that everyone has a right to a place called home.

When we examine the concept *home*, however, it becomes more and more elusive, and when we ask people in general to define a home, they will usually begin by describing a house or flat. Certainly a home must have a physical embodiment, such as bricks and mortar, and certainly it has to be a place, but equally certainly the physical framework does not constitute a home.

The inspiration and the seedbed for Focus Point was a group of women who were out-of-home, with whom I lived and worked eleven years ago. When I talked with them and listened to them about the experience of being out-of-home, it became very clear to me that a home is more than a roof over one's head—though a place without a roof wouldn't qualify as a home. They said that being without a home meant being without safety and security, being without dignity and respect. They were saying very clearly that a home is a place in which to feel safe and secure, warm and dry and protected; to be oneself, to rest and eat, sleep and be entertained, love and laugh, argue and cry, read a book, share a meal, watch a television programme, play an instrument, do a bit of gardening, play with the kids, have a drink, get the housework done and the bills paid; to be at ease with oneself and with one's family and friends, without fear of intrusion or interference.

Shelter may be the first constituent of a home, but it is not the only one. It is not enough to give a person a bed for the night in order to deal with their homelessness. Giving them a bed they can count on being there again the next night is a step in the right direction, but it is still not enough. Being without a home is being without that place in which to be oneself, at ease, secure and at rest. The need for a place like that is deep and urgent in all of us.

What sort of people are deprived of a home? The fact is that anyone—or at least anyone who is not financially very secure—can become homeless for a variety of reasons. A young person for whom life has become intolerable in the family home, to the point of feeling there is no alternative but to move out, even with nowhere to go, is likely to become homeless very quickly, moving from one friend's house to another, and then on to hostels and squats and finally, in all probability, the streets. A woman who flees from a violent husband may be lucky enough to get a place in a hostel for battered wives but a temporary arrangement like that is not a home, especially not for a woman with children. A single man, or one separated from his wife, who is made redundant and arrives back in Dublin from England looking for somewhere to live is unlikely to be housed by the local authorities in his native place and has quite a high chance of becoming homeless. A family where the main breadwinner loses his or her job and the family income takes a sudden drop, with the result that the rent or mortgage can no longer be paid, is at risk of at least temporary homelessness. A woman whose husband dies, if that husband is the breadwinner, and particularly if the family home is 'tied' accommodation, going with the husband's job, can find herself and her children on the streets very quickly. It can happen to anyone.

For most people who lose their home, if the response is quick and targeted, being out-of-home is a transitory *stage* in their lives. For some people, however, the response to their homelessness is not quick and appropriate to their needs, and for them homelessness can develop into a permanent *state*, a way of living constantly on the margins of society, with no hope of ever re-entering the mainstream and having a place to call home to act as a secure base from which to live a normal life. It is Focus Point Ireland's ambition to ensure that homelessness is only a passing stage in people's lives and is not allowed to develop into a permanent state.

Focus Point Ireland is immensely grateful to the writers who generously gave of their talent to make this book such a treasury of reflections on home. I very much hope that it will provoke in at least some of its readers an empathy with those who are out-of-home, wandering abroad, lost, displaced, trapped in the culture of the streets with all its dangers or living precarious lives moving from hostel to hostel, doss to doss, friend to friend, ever in danger that they too may end up on the streets. I hope these writings will deepen readers' understanding of the great human emotional deprivation it is to be without a place to call home.

Finally, in addition to the writers, I would like to thank all the other people who made this book possible: the publishers, A. & A. Farmar; Siobhán Parkinson, Mary Jennings and Rachel Collier of Focus Point Ireland; and Irish Permanent plc, who kindly supported the publication of the book.

Stanislaus Kennedy, RSC
President, Focus Point Ireland

Acknowledgements

The royalties that would otherwise accrue from sales of this volume have generously been donated by the authors to Focus Point Ireland for its work in preventing and alleviating homelessness. Focus Point Ireland and the publishers thank the authors most sincerely for their generosity in this regard.

PUBLICATION DETAILS

John Banville, 'What a Surprise the Familiar Is', excerpt from *The Book of Evidence*, published by Minerva

Eavan Boland, 'A Ballad of Home', from *Night Feed*, published by Carcanet

Clare Boylan, excerpt from 'A Little Girl, Never Out Before', from *Concerning Virgins*, published by Penguin Books

Dermot Bolger, 'A Place of Streams', excerpt from *The Journey Home*, published by Penguin Books

Polly Devlin, 'Our Cohesion', excerpt from *All of Us There*, published by The Blackstaff Press

Emma Donoghue's story 'The Tale of the Cottage' will be published by Hamish Hamilton in *Kissing the Witch* in 1997

Paul Durcan, 'Windfall', from *Collected Poems*, published by The Blackstaff Press

Anne Enright, 'The House of the Architect's Love Story', from *The Portable Virgin,* published by Minerva

Vona Groarke, 'Home', from *Shale*, by kind permission of the author and The Gallery Press

Hugo Hamilton, 'The Irish Worker', from *Dublin Where the Palm Trees Grow*, published by Faber & Faber Ltd

Dermot Healy, 'Geese and Orchards', excerpt from *The Goat's Song*, published by Harvill Collins

Seamus Heaney, 'Sunlight' from 'Mossbawn: Two Poems in Dedication', from *New Selected Poems* published by Faber & Faber Ltd; and 'Sweeney's Lament in Mourne', an excerpt from *Sweeney Astray*, published by Faber & Faber Ltd

Jennifer Johnston, 'Charming Red Brick Residence', excerpt from *The Illusionist*, published by Sinclair Stevenson

Brendan Kennelly, 'We are living' reprinted by permission of Bloodaxe Books Ltd from *A Time for Voices* by Brendan Kennelly (Bloodaxe Books 1990)

Mary Lavin, 'Tom', from *Mary O'Grady*, published by Virago

Michael Longley, 'Epithalamion' and 'Architecture', from *Poems 1963–1983*, published by Secker and Warburg

Joan McBreen, 'The Wind Beyond the Wall' from *The Wind Beyond the Wall*, published by Storyline Press (USA), and 'On Hearing my Daughter Play "The Swan"', from *A Walled Garden in Moylough,* published by Salmon Publishing

Eugene McCabe, 'Roma', from *Heritage*, published by Gollancz; available in Ireland in an O'Brien Press edition

Colum McCann, 'Fishing the Sloe Black River', from *Fishing the Sloe Black River*, published by Phoenix House

Paula Meehan, 'Home', from *Pillow Talk*, by kind permission of the author and The Gallery Press

Éiléan Ní Chuilleanáin, 'The House Remembered', from *The Second Voyage* (1986) and 'Party Wall', from *The Brazen Serpent* (1994), by kind permission of the author and The Gallery Press

Joseph O'Connor, 'How to be Irish in London', from *The Secret World of the Irish Male*, published by New Island Books

The Authors

THE AUTHORS

Ivy Bannister writes plays and fiction. Her collection of short stories, *Magician*, has just been published.

John Banville is an award-winning novelist and literary editor of *The Irish Times*. His novels include *Ghosts* and *The Newton Letter*. *The Book of Evidence* was shortlisted for the Booker Prize.

Also a poet and novelist, **Sebastian Barry** is best known for his plays, in particular the highly acclaimed *The Steward of Christendom*.

Eavan Boland is one of Ireland's leading poets. Her books include *Collected Poems* and *Object Lessons*, a prose collection.

Dermot Bolger is a publisher as well as a writer and is best known for his novels *The Journey Home* and *Emily's Shoes* and for his award-winning plays.

As well as writing fiction, **Clare Boylan** is well known as a journalist and broadcaster. Her books include *Holy Pictures* and *That Bad Woman*.

Writer-in-residence at the Abbey Theatre, the young writer **Marina Carr** is best known for her plays *The Mai* and *Portia Coughlan*.

Roz Cowman lectures in the Department of Adult Education in UCC and has received the Patrick Kavanagh Award for poetry.

Polly Devlin is well known as a journalist and broadcaster as well as a fiction writer. Her books include *The Far Side of the Lough* and *Dora*.

Emma Donoghue is best known for her novels *Stir-Fry* and *Hood*. She also writes plays and is the author of *Passions Between Women: British Lesbian Culture, 1668–1801*.

Mary Dorcey's most recent collection of poems is *The River that Carries Me*, and she has also published a collection of short stories, *A Noise from the Woodshed*.

One of Ireland's most popular poets, **Paul Durcan** is well known for his readings of his own work. His books include *A Snail in His Prime* and *Christmas Day*.

Anne Enright's first novel is *The Wig my Father Wore*, and she is working on a second. She is also known for her work in television and radio.

The young writer **Eleanor Flegg** has completed her first novel and is working on a second. She recently received a Hennessy Award for her short story 'Daniel in Babylon'.

Vona Groarke is a former holder of the *Sunday Tribune* Young Writer of the Year Award. *Shale* is her first collection.

Hugo Hamilton's family ties with Germany influence the themes and settings of such novels as *The Last Shot* and *The Love Test*.

Dermot Healy's novel *The Goat's Song* received great acclaim. *The Bend for Home* has just been published.

The poetry of the Nobel laureate **Seamus Heaney** enjoys unusual popular appeal. His latest collection is *The Spirit Level*.

Desmond Hogan is the author of five novels, including *A Farewell to Prague* and *The Ikon Maker*.

Jennifer Johnston is widely acclaimed as one of Ireland's finest novelists. Her most recent novel, *The Illusionist*, was published earlier this year.

Maeve Kelly's books include the novel *Florrie's Girls* and *Orange Horses*, a collection of short stories.

Brendan Kennelly is as well known for his public persona and as a lecturer at Trinity College as for his poetry. His latest book is *Poetry My Arse*.

Sadly, **Mary Lavin** died earlier this year. She was the acknowledged doyenne of the Irish short story. Her collections include *Tales from Bective Bridge* and *In a Café*.

Michael Longley is one of Ulster's finest lyricists. His recent collections include *Gorse Fires* and *The Ghost Orchid*.

Joan McBreen, a primary teacher by profession, is now a working poet. Her two collections are *The Wind Beyond the Wall* and *A Walled Garden in Moylough*.

Eugene McCabe lives on a County Monaghan farm and has recently begun to publish again after a long silence. His novels include *Death and Nightingales*.

Patrick McCabe's novel *The Butcher Boy* won an *Irish Times*/Aer Lingus award and was short-listed for the Booker Prize. *The Dead School* is his latest novel.

The award-winning writer **Colum McCann** lives in New York and Dublin, and is the author of the novel *Songdogs*. His second novel will be published soon.

Catherine Phil MacCarthy's first book is *This Hour of the Tide* and she is currently working on a second collection and on a collaborative project for the City Arts Office.

Medhbh McGuckian's elliptical poems have brought her wide acclaim. Her latest collections are *Ballycastle on the Beach* and *Captain Lavender*.

Frank McGuinness's best-known plays include *Observe the Sons of Ulster Marching to the Somme* and *The Bird Sanctuary*. He has also published a collection of poems, *Booterstown*.

John MacKenna's books include *Clare*, a novel based on the life of John Clare, and *A Year in Our Lives*, a collection of short stories. He is also a radio producer.

Aisling Maguire is a freelance editor and writer. Her first novel, *Breaking Out*, was published this year.

Paula Meehan is that rare phenomenon—a best-selling poet. Her two collections are *The Man who was Marked by Winter* and *Pillow Talk*.

Máire Mhac an tSaoi is the doyenne of Irish-language poetry. *An Cion go dtí Seo* is her collected poems, and a new selection will be published shortly.

Éiléan Ní Chuilleanáin is highly respected as one of Ireland's major poets. She has several collections, the most recent of which is *The Brazen Serpent*.

The Irish-language poet **Nuala Ní Dhomhnaill's** practice of publishing also in translation has made her work accessible to a wide audience. Her most recent collections are *The Astrakhan Cloak* and *Pharaoh's Daughter*.

Clairr O'Connor is a poet, a writer of fiction and a teacher. Her novels are *Belonging* and *Love in Another Room*, and she also writes radio plays.

Joseph O'Connor is well known to *Sunday Tribune* readers for his humorous journalism. His most recent novel is *Desperadoes*.

Mary O'Donnell's books include *Reading the Sunflowers in September*, a collection of poems, and *The Light Makers*, a novel. *Virgin and the Boy* is her most recent book.

James Ryan's first novel, *Home from England*, was very well received and is to be filmed. He is working on his second novel.

The novelist **Colm Tóibín** is also well known for his non-fiction, including *The Sign of the Cross*. His most recent novel is *The Story of the Night*.

William Trevor is a master of the Irish short story as well as being an insightful and disturbing novelist. His latest novel is *Felicia's Journey*, winner of the 1994 Whitbread award.

MacDara Woods has published several poetry collections, and his

Selected Poems was published this year.

Siobhán Parkinson studied for her doctorate at Trinity College Dublin and is a children's writer, best known for her novel *Amelia*. She is an editor and technical writer by profession and combines her work as editor with Focus Point Ireland with a freelance career.

PART 1

The

House Remembered

The House Remembered

ÉILÉAN NÍ CHUILLEANÁIN

The house persists, the permanent
Scaffolding while the stones move round.
Convolvulus winds the bannisters, sucks them down;
We found an icicle under the stairs
Tall as a church candle;
It refused to answer questions
But proved its point by freezing hard.

The house changes, the stones
Choking in dry lichen stupidly spreading
Abusing the doorposts, frost on the glass.
Nothing stays still, the house is still the same
But the breast over the sink turned into a tap
And coming through the door all fathers look the same.

The stairs and windows waver but the house stands up;
Peeling away the walls another set shows through.
I can't remember, it all happened too recently.
But somebody was born in every room.

The Party Wall

We were all still living at home then,
In the house with the fancy grilles
And the tall iron gates that let us out
Gliding to business and back at night for our tea.
We rose one morning to find the garden
Drifted and crisped with stiff white feathers.
They shone bluish against the red brick walls,
As they shifted and settled in the draught from the street.

We were not shocked at all until the next day
When the aerial photographs were published
Showing the house that backed against ours
But looked away across the Avenue
Visited the same, its roof and courtyards
Blessed with angeldown and cobalt shadows.

The tenants had my grandfather's name.
I went on my bicycle to see Father Deveney
In his room in the old priests' home.
We sat at the window looking towards Mount Desert
And he ate sweets and told me he remembered
When that house too had been part of his parish.
But he had never been told of my aunt's story
About the trouble over building the party wall.

The Diary of Jane Campbell

FRANK MCGUINNESS

After Ammi Phillips, itinerant painter of portraits,
San Diego, California

My mother and I stitch calico
For curtains. My grandmother too.
These save our house from the sun.
My mother's name is Sarah;
I am seven, I cradle a doll.
It looks like me and my mother.
My body's a frock, red as Mama's face.
The painter who saw me saw that.

Calico, embroidered with lace,
My mother touches—how delicate.
I love her. Mama is delicate.
She may well die in childbirth, but
I will cover this continent seeking
Her; transformed by an itinerant painter,
My geometry America, my compass myself.
This is the diary of Jane Campbell.

I count the pieces of my life
In the brown crystal ball of
My country. I'll marry for life and
Have seven children, all with my eyes.
The hunter who trapped me forever,
That painter, had eyes, eyes like a
Needle stitching calico for a shroud,
But not mine. Not Jane Campbell.

In My Father's Garage

IVY BANNISTER

My father's work gloves wait for him in the garage on the bench that he built himself, the shapes of his hands still giving the gloves form, their leather fingers worn to bald by his honest endeavour. For he was a worker—my father—ever industrious, putting his back whole-heartedly into the tasks of house and garden.

It is a vast space, my father's garage, always airy, even in the burning heat of a Connecticut summer. Inside, there's a wood-pile, cut and laid by himself, each log in perfect relation to the next. Nearby, a shiny power mower rests, six hundred dollars' worth of gleaming blade and steel, bought as much to keep my father going as to cut the grass.

But underfoot the dead leaves rustle in my father's garage.

A canoe is upended over a pair of sawhorses. It is nearly a hundred years old, that canoe. Inside, its wooden fretwork gleams. I run my hand along the keel, where the canvas is cracking now, and I remember how well my father taught me to manage that canoe Indian-style, to steer swiftly and silently, through the whispering grasses of the salt marsh behind our home.

Poor Daddy.

Near the canoe, there's an over-sized wheelbarrow, as blue as my father's eyes. It's the wheelbarrow in which he shifted tons of paving stones, cement and sand, in the days when he built patios, walls and raised gardens. I used to hide in that same wheelbarrow under a mountain of autumn leaves, to leap up like a Jack-in-the-box, and my father would yelp with surprise, never once complaining about the scattered leaves.

He was the salt of the earth, my father.

On the walls in the garage hang his tools, utilitarian and old-fashioned, built solidly to last forever. A mallet hammer, a pitch-fork and shovel, a clawed rake on a seven-foot handle, a massive two-handled saw for cutting down trees. Tools that he used, then painstakingly oiled and cleaned, before returning them to their proper place.

There are hoses coiled by his hand, and balls of grey twine, neatly husbanded, for my father wasted nothing. There are jars, clouded with dust, of meticulously sorted nails. There are barrels and basins and buckets. Bags of fertiliser and weed killer and garden mulch, splitting now from age, allowing their contents to trickle onto the floor, in a way that my father would not have countenanced.

And lest it be imagined that my father never played, there are fishing rods and tackle; and tennis rackets, their gut yellow with age. There are horseshoes for tossing, and ancient snow shoes, huge fish-shaped frames woven with leather, in which my father, as a young man, stalked the snowdrifts of New Hampshire, nearly a lifetime ago.

Only there, on a shelf, neatly stacked, are my father's cigar boxes—all empty—but solid and serviceable still. Cuesta-Rey No. 95, the boxes say. Cuesta-Rey, The Finest Tobacco. As I take one down, a puff of dust rises into the air. And as that dust drifts through the lazy afternoon, I can smell again the smoke. His smoke. The smoke of the cigars that he loved, Cuesta-Rey No. 95.

It fills my head that smoke, and suddenly I realise that there is more of my father here in this garage than there is in that place where he lives now. That place, some thirty miles down the road, where my father suffers, no longer patient nor kind, but an unruly stranger of eighty years and more, harnessed into a chair, an ailing giant whose brain has died while his angry body lives on, imprisoned in the fog of dementia.

Our Cohesion

POLLY DEVLIN

Our cohesion is not just a matter of a close family feeling or material connections. An outside influence or presence joins us together too, holds us literally in place—Muinterevlin, that ragged, low-lying, silent place in which we were born—and, however we move, the place runs in on us as though to hold us tighter. We still converge on it as often as possible and, as we journey down the Moor Hill Road, we listen for the first distant sound of the water. As soon as we can hear it we know we are home, however permanent the place we have come from appears to be. For all of us the lough defines that place on the interior map which makes home uniquely home, so that any other place can always only be somewhere else: a simulacrum of the real place and outside our imaginative grasp.

The name of our townland, one of the thirty that make up the Parish of Ardboe, is Muinterevlin, meaning in Gaelic 'the country of the Devlins', and the land over which we roam is composed of a body-mould of our forebears, dug and turned into the earth, fertilizing it, flavouring it, the very soil steeped in us, the surface exuding an aura and an odour of *us*. The old and heavy earth there seems to be as alive as we are, powered by a different kind of life motion, one that is infinitely slower, each heartbeat lasting decades, but to which we are connected. I sometimes think that if I could put my ear to it at the right time I might catch the throb, just as one glittering day I will see the flower on Lizzie's peony that only blooms every seven years, or find the apocryphal piece of wood petrified into stone by the lough water that I buried each year so long ago.

Muinterevlin reaches further into the lough than any other of the small fingers of land along the shore, all of which tentatively dip in to the water as though not sure of the welcome or depth and then dissolve gently into sedgy watery swamp before giving into the water. The edges are held down by boulders, tussocks, osiers and rushes. Just where Muinterevlin reaches the water it suddenly rears up, into Ardboe Point. It is the only hill on the long side of the lough shore and on its very tip stands the Cross reputed to have been built by St Colman and his monks in the seventh century. Behind it, a small graveyard surrounds the ruins of the monks' small church and almost vanished abbey. The graveyard is our magic playground and the Cross pins it to the ground.

The word Ardboe means 'high cow' in Gaelic, and the most romantic and most often repeated explanation for the name is that the mortar used for building the Cross and church was mixed with the milk of a magic cow, which gave it its staying power. Whatever the source of the liquid used to build the Cross and church, cow milk or lough water, it has been standing there, as we believe, on the only eminence within ten miles, for over thirteen hundred years. The position of the small primitive group of holy buildings silhouetted against water and sky affects us, and most visitors, to initial stillness and silence. The crumbling arched windows frame the perpetual movement of the small crested waves of the lough, and more often than not the two white swans who nest on the Rock Shore, further round from the Cross Point, swim within the serene arched frame.

The Celtic Cross is an extraordinary monument, towering twenty feet and more above us. It is made of massive stone blocks, and each of the four sides of each great block are carved into panels illustrating episodes from the Bible and the Apocrypha. These carvings were once sharp and detailed but are now blurred into indentations and soft shapelessness by the rain and wind of a millennium. . . . In the 1930s, an official caretaker was appointed to look after the Cross, the graveyard and the abbey. The job was given to an old great-uncle (everyone in the district is inter-related) who is known for some lost reason as the Needle. He knows the arcane meanings and allegories illustrated in each panel of the Cross, and expounds them in a version handed down orally over the centuries. He is sensible to a fault of his official position and the standing it gives him—or he thinks ought to give him—in the community. He is the official expounder of the meaning of the Cross: its reading.

Returned emigrants, amateur archaeologists, strangers out for a day's jaunt, historians or scholars can easily prevail on him to read it, but it would not occur to him to read it to us, nor to us to ask him. We know he would think it a conceit, a waste of time, so what we learn is what we overhear. Since the Needle speaks our strong local dialect, few listeners from outside the parish can understand more than a few words, but no one's enjoyment seems to be lessened by this lack of comprehension.

The Needle is usually either leaning on his gate watching his small world meander or cycle by, or is sitting on one of the tombstones surveying the lough and keeping an eye out for the water bailiff. Whenever anyone deemed worthy of having the Cross read arrives at its base, he leaves his vantage point and hurries to the Cross. Getting the keys from about his person is a business: he plunges about the waist and pockets of his ancient trousers and coats, scrabbling among pieces of fishing-line, impaling his fingers on eel-hooks, invoking the Holy Family under his breath and asking St Anthony to help him—this kind of search is called 'hoking'. Finally he finds the keys, opens the padlocked iron gate set into the rails with considerable flourish, steps in, closes the gate and looks out grandly at those left outside the barricade. Favoured visitors are occasionally allowed in with him to look more closely at the carvings. We are permanently banished and lurk outside, derisive but fascinated.

One memorable day I found the padlocked gate open and crept in, thrilled and fearful. The great Cross loomed high above me. The road past Treanor's towards our house looked different viewed through bars. I put my hand on the warm stone of the Cross for the first time and suddenly the Needle stepped out from behind it. I leapt with guilt. 'Get out,' he said, 'and away up the road with you, you skitter. You're like a musheroon. You couldn't be watched. You're not there one time, but the next time you look you were there all the while.'

We spend a great deal of our time—as much as we can get away from school—by the Old Cross and down by the lough shore. To reach it is a matter of walking four hundred yards along that road edged with a prodigal quantity of wild grasses, fruits and flowers. Hawthorn tumbles over bramble and wild roses, and below these bushes, sedges and wild strawberries grow profusely as well as sorrel, which we eat as part of our daily diet, examining each leaf with deep suspicion for the foamy signs of cuckoo sally. Odium attaches to eating this. We think the foam harbours worms, or rather that it breeds them, that they spring from the foam itself.

The dusty road, one way and the other, for all its shortness links us to nearly everything that is significant in our geography and landscape, connecting with the Cross and dribbling round the outskirts of the newly-built aerodrome. It widens as it leads towards the more populated and civilised part of Ardboe parish, where it ceases to be our psychic territorial property, our trail, and becomes only another road. That road to the Cross, unravelling so timidly between the fields, often had an undiscovered look with its dusty surface in summer or pot-holed, muddy and rutted in winter. Long after most other roads in the country are black and gleaming in their tarmac coverings, ours is still untouched because Lizzie Treanor, who owns the stretch of road that leads to the Cross, refuses to allow it to be tarmacked. Like Barbara Freitchie, she stands defiant, her nine dogs swirling around her, a cigarette dangling from her mouth, swearing at the steam-roller and its hapless driver, an employee of the County Council who has never been this far into the hinterland before.

We, who are sitting like a row of gremlins on the old Cross mound under its railings, cannot get over this. It is an apocalyptic moment. No one in our experience has ever conceived of defying authority, and for Lizzie to be defying the Government in the shape of a steam-roller seems the most astonishingly foolhardy act. We wait for her come-uppance, for the police to arrive, not leisurely on their bikes as they sometimes do but swooping out of lorries to bear her away. None of this happens: the bemused man driving the steam-roller turns his green and silver monster and goes rolling back up the road, squishing out the surplus tar at each side of the road like an overfilled sandwich, to get some further authority for proceeding. There is no further authority for a while, until finally the County Council slaps a requisition order on the road and has it tarred into conformity, while Lizzie stares, baleful, baffled, from her windows.

Along the length of the road, tarred and untarred, sleeping dogs lie like punctuation. Each house has at least one dog attached to it. They are not house pets, but are tolerated and fed scraps. These dogs all have a lean and feral look, and even when they appear to be in a deep sleep in the middle of the road they sense our approach and twitch a tail in greeting and goodwill.

There were only six or seven houses along that stretch of road leading in the opposite direction from the Cross towards the Cross Roads; most of them are set back from the road up in the rampars and fields, at the end of grassy lanes which we call loanings. Like many in the parish, all these houses are built in the local traditional style: long, low, and white-washed with lime inside and out. They have only one outside door, which is made in two halves, the bottom half always closed against dogs and draughts and over which, if you're tall enough, you can lean for a bit of a crack or to pass the time of day with anyone passing who is temperamentally and psychologically capable of speech. Just inside this door there is a jamb wall to stop the draught from blowing into the kitchen as well as to make a tiny hallway, and all walls, inside and out, are over a foot thick and sliced by small deep windows. There are no more than three rooms in all such houses, including the kitchen, and no inside bathrooms or lavatories; yet many contain families of ten or twelve people of all ages and generations . . .

The walls of these long, low, shared houses are thick enough— made as they are of mud and stone—to prevent any noise seeping through and, although there are no hedges or fences between the two houses, each family has a strict regard for physical boundaries. Most of the houses in the district look at one with the surrounding landscape and the earth in which they are almost rooted, since they have been built out of the clay beneath them. They look like moulds for houses, rather than the houses themselves.

There are a few notable exceptions to this intimate organic

style of local houses. First the pair of tiny cottages built by the Tyrone County Council in 1926: one for the Needle, as part of his job as caretaker of the Cross, in which he lives with his wife and at one time with their ten children, who are all now grown-up and have emigrated, and the other for his brother and equally large family, only two of whom are left at home. These cottages have a mean and alien look with their flung grey pebble-dash clinging so scantily to the rigid four-square walls, although in-side they are much lighter than the traditional houses, because of their bigger aluminium windows which open outwards.

Then there's our house, which is the biggest in the townland, a two-storey Edwardian affair with bathrooms, a breakfast-room, a sitting and dining-room. Most exceptional of all, it is surrounded by a large garden, lawns and orchards. My grandfather, who built the house, used the biggest and best of the fields of his small farm to make his house and garden, and in a place where families are so large and land is so scarce such prodigality is extraordinary. In later years we speculate that this house and garden with its orchards, chestnut trees and conifers—alien trees in the landscape—its big lawn, its drive cutting through lugubrious laurels to wrought-iron gates hanging on squat stone pillars topped by spheres, must have seemed like the height of pretension to my grand-father's peers and kin, who would on the whole have wished him ill rather than well, albeit in a mild way. It is often the way of those who have been exploited by outsiders to begrudge suc-cess to their own kind.

The Kitchen Window

ROZ COWMAN

The Sunday mutton turns
in its pepper muslin
these June evenings.
Milk in the pantry breaks
into cirro-cumulus.
Talk pooters
between home and office,
is lost in a backyard's dusk

What lies beyond the glass hills
is chatoyancy, and lures
like an old land
seen through a mullion.
You will not cross those hills again
now the equinox is done.

Caves eat the liver
of a sandstone hill where you watch
the flight of the photons,
space-like separate,
each
aware of the other.

Home Daughter

MEDBH MCGUCKIAN

Ever-refreshing golden upper sky,
twelve heads from a frieze are brushed on to you
just like a morning kiss, just whitening
with winter passage rain.

Graded sky devoted to justice,
seventeenth-century people from a red-figured vase
become your monthly furniture,
give their names to your clouds.

A cylinder of moving human beings
confiscated from a Sung bowl
cut off the King's English sky with a knife,
look at lands on a marriage tray.

A Place of Streams

DERMOT BOLGER

Where does our story begin? The first morning I crossed the park to work? No, even before then our paths would have crossed. How often did our parents pass on the main street of the village while the labourers' cottages were being bulldozed and the estates, like a besieging army, began to ring the green post office, the pub with the skittle alley, the old graveyard with its shambling vaults? But my parents and Shay's would not have mixed, being from different worlds, with different sets of experiences. I think of my parents, younger than I can really imagine them, taking the single-decker bus out beyond the cemetery, returning, as they thought, to the familiar hawthorn bushes and streams, to the sanctuary of the countryside. Shay used to laugh about how his father cursed the Corporation for casting them out into exile, complaining about bus fares to work in the brewery he had always walked to, bewildered by the dark lanes behind his house without the shouts of neighbours or the reassuring bustle of traffic.

Years later my father told me that the Church of Ireland built my estate, some half-arsed scheme for a Protestant colony among the fields. They couldn't fill it from their own flock so the likes of my parents were allowed to pay their deposit and transport their country habits from bedsits along the canal back to the laneways again. A place of streams I'm told it was, each in turn piped underground as more people came. Once a row of gardens collapsed to reveal the water running underneath.

They planted trees in the image of their lost homeland, put down potato beds, built timber hen-houses. I woke to the sound of chicks escaping through the wire mesh to scamper among rows of vegetables. A dozen streets away Shay must have woken to the noise of pigeon lofts, that city man's sport, backyards ringing with displaced Dublin accents. Briefly we played in the same school yard before he was expelled, though neither of us remembered the other. We spoke of it in awe as from another century; the monstrous thug of a vice-principal wasting with cancer among his array of canes; the tricolour flown from the mast beside the concrete steps; the screeching of seagulls which hovered, waiting for boys to be drilled into lines and marched to class, before swooping to fight over the littered bread. I wish I could remember Shay there, those all-important two years older than me, among the swarm of lads stomping after a plastic ball. But I can recall little beyond a hubbub of noise; the stink of fish from a ten-year-old who helped his mother in the processing plant each evening; the twins who shared one pair of plastic sandals for a week, each one barefoot on alternate days. And the ease with which, among such crowds, I could remain invisible. I can still repeat the roll-call of nine-year-old future factory hands and civil servants, but it's myself that I cannot properly recall. I was like some indistinct embryonic creature, a negative through which nobody had ever shone light. Was I happy or sad? I have no memories of being anything more than a sleepwalker feigning the motions of life, living through the black-and-white rays of the television screen.

Each evening my father came in from Plunkett Motors, took his spade from the shed, and joined the chorus of rural accents across the ruck of hedgerows. I'd hide among the alder bushes bordering the hen run to watch the men dig and weed with the expertise of country hands, while my mother washed clothes by hand in the sink, light from the open kitchen door filtering through the lilac. I felt that square of earth was home, a green expanse formed by the row of long gardens. I'd pull the branches close to me while across the suburb Shay played among the red-brick terraces built by the Corporation. The gardens there were tiny with hardly space for a shed. Shay's gang would scatter with their football if a squad car showed, then resume their games on the next concrete street, voices still calling when only the vaguest shapes could be seen dodging between the street lamps.

We grew up divided by only a few streets so you'd think we would share a background. Yet somehow we didn't. At least not then, not till later when we found we were equally dispossessed. *The children of limbo* was how Shay called us once. We came from nowhere and found we belonged nowhere else. Those gardens I called home were a retreat from the unknown world. When the radio announcer gave the results of the provincial Gaelic matches the backs would straighten, neighbours reverting to county allegiances as they slagged each other. *And remember, if you feel like singing, do sing an Irish song*, the presenter of the Walton's programme urged and, as the strains of 'Kelly, the boy from Killane' and 'The Star of the County Down' crackled from the radio, all the stooping figures who knew the words by heart hummed them in their minds, reassured of who they were no matter what incomprehensible things were occurring outside.

As long as I remained among the hens and barking dogs I too could belong, but each walk home from school by the new shopping arcades, each programme on the television religiously switched on at half five in every terraced house, was thrusting me out into my own time. I began bringing home phrases that couldn't fit in that house when we still knelt for the family rosary. I hid photographs of rock stars beneath my mattress like pornographic pictures, wrote English soccer players' names on my copy book feeling I was committing an act of betrayal.

When I was twelve my father brought me back to the farm bordering the Kerry coast where he had been born. I stood awkwardly in my city clothes, kicking a football back and forth to my cousins across the yard. None of us spoke as we eyed each other suspiciously and waited for our parents to finish reminiscing. Next morning before dawn he took me out to the milking shed lit by a bare bulb. I never saw him so relaxed as when he bent with ease to squeeze the teats, glancing back proudly, urging me to grasp the teats of a huge lurching cow I was frightened of. For the first time I felt the division between us.

I didn't understand it then, but I grew up in perpetual exile; from my parents when on the streets, from my own world when at home. Once Shay told me about visiting his uncles and great aunts left behind in the Liberties. They welcomed him like a returned *émigré* to the courtyards of squalid Victorian flats and led him around the ramshackle streets choked with traffic, pity-ing him the open spaces of the distant roads he played on.

How can you learn self-respect if you're taught that where you live is not your real home? At fourteen I tried to bridge the gap by journeying out into my father's uncharted countryside. I'd rise before dawn to cook myself breakfast and when I ate at the kitchen table he would come down to place money on the oil-cloth beside me and watch from the doorway as I set off to find Ireland. I arrived home with reports he couldn't comprehend; long-haired Germans in battered vans picking up hikers; skinheads battling outside chip shops in Athlone. Then came the final betrayal of something even he couldn't define when, at fifteen, I chose the first friend of my own. 'That old Protestant woman' my father always called her, though she had not been inside any church for half a century.

Looking back, my life was like a candle, briefly sparked into flame in that old woman's caravan among the fields, and extin-guished again until I met Shay. The years between speed up— the new intimacy of class-mates in the months before exams; nights studying in each other's houses; weekends stumbling home drunk on two pints from town. I had been a loner before, so used to solitude I didn't understand what loneliness was. But that last year in school I felt enclosed in the company of friends, finally seeming to belong somewhere.

On the night of the final exam we walked out to Mother Plunkett's Cabin at Kilshane Cross, were barred before closing time and staggered home through country lanes off the North Road in hysterical laughter. After that I rarely saw them again, the release from school shattering our intimacy, leaving us half-embarrassed when we met, reliving the same stale memories. That autumn passed into winter. Sometimes I cadged the money for dances; mostly I just walked the streets putting off my re-turn home. Some mornings polite rejections of my application forms for work lay like poisoned fish washed up on the hall floor, but normally I stared down at an empty, mocking square of lino, and began the same futile rounds of the industrial es-tates.

I thought my father would never let the garden run to seed even as he grew older, but that year after school I watched it happen without comprehending. The world of the gardens had changed. Where neighbours once kept the city out with hedgerows and chickens, now they used broken glass cemented into concrete walls. A decade had worked its influence. The alder bushes were gone, the last of the hens butchered. Patios had appeared with crazy paving, mock Grecian fonts made of plastic, and everywhere, like a frozen river, concrete reigned. Porches had sprung up bearing ludicrous names, Ashbrook, Riverglade, The Dell, each neighbour jockeying to be the first to discard their past. Only our garden had remained untouched, the potato beds becoming overgrown and the roof caving in on the felt-covered hut where my hands had once searched for eggs in straw.

Every evening that winter my father's face was like ash, gathered from a burnt-out half-century and spread in a fine crust over his bones. His eyes were more jaded than any I had ever known. He'd come home from work with stories of Pascal Plunkett's moods, collapse into an armchair by the television and stare at his idle eldest son. He said little and I learnt to match his words. We sat in a silence broken only by my mother's fussing, while outside the weeds and nettles choked his dreams. Sometimes he'd cough and, looking up, ask me to chop everything down. 'Tomorrow,' I'd say. 'I'm tired now.' I would mean to put on his rubber boots, take the tools hanging between nails in the shed and walk out as I used to watch him do, but those photocopied rejections seemed to have sapped my strength. I sulked instead, brooding on the few words that passed between us, although it wasn't what he said that hurt but the disbelief in his eyes when I'd mention all the places I had tried for work. In the end I just said nothing. The present made no sense in his world. He stared blankly at the evening news while they carried the victims of the bombings and hijackings away in black plastic sacks.

Christmas froze into January. Blue nights alone in the overgrown garden, making tea in the kitchen at three in the morning. That year had become a posthumous existence. At night I'd smoke joints in the bathroom, leaning on my toes to blow the smoke out the window, constantly alert for an opening door. I seemed to have lost the power to sleep, gradually losing track of the everyday world. February came and then March, fresh weeds squeezing through the dead grass.

At two o'clock one morning I walked down the garden, wading through weeds like a field of barley. Lines of new extensions stretched on both sides, a lone light burning in a garage twelve doors down. I thought of Jews hiding in cellars, snatching only a few seconds of air before dawn. Now I slept while others worked, rose in the afternoons, seemed to come to life only when darkness came. I had fallen from the cycle of life, with no longer the will-power to struggle. The queues each Tuesday afternoon, men pushing like a human battering ram against the door of the employment exchange. The letters posted out sending one hundred people for interview for a single job that I had to attend in case they checked up and cut my assistance. The fear of daring to hope in case it turned to bitterness when I was turned down; the hatred of leaving the bed and having to face the empty letter rack in the hall.

I turned to go back inside and saw my father standing at the gate beneath the arc of bare lilac bushes. At first I thought it was an apparition from the past. He had pulled on a white shirt and a pair of trousers held up by ancient braces. I walked towards him in the blue moonlight, both of us embarrassed, neither knowing how to talk.

'What's going to happen to you, son?'

His voice was low, humble with bewilderment. I would have liked to touch his shoulder, to somehow reassure him. Looking at him I knew that I would leave home soon, that only poverty was keeping me there. Ever since our fight about the old woman in the fields we had both lost the simple ease which had once existed between us. I knew that he was thinking about days further back, times I'd waited beside the lilac bushes wanting to feel important, hoping he'd ask me to fetch some tool from the shed. I longed to say, *Tomorrow dad, we'll take those tools down, fix up the garden the way it used to be.* But I couldn't. I had to turn away.

'I don't know. You go back to bed now. I'm just getting some air.'

He shook his head and I watched him turn and walk up the path. There was a nettle swaying near my hand. I pressed my fingers over it. It stung badly, but at least the pain felt real.

Then one morning, grey and ordinary, a letter from the Voters' Register's office came. The offer was a temporary position starting on the first of the month. I felt there should be bands marching from the kitchen, majorettes turning somersaults on the lino. Instead my mother was scrubbing floors in Plunkett Undertakers, my brothers and sisters were at school. Happiness seemed to underline my isolation. I went out into the street hoping to meet somebody I could share the news with. Behind the supermarket I saw my father in the forecourt of Plunkett Motors. Younger men asked him questions as they stripped an engine. He pulled on his cigarette, coughed and spat on the tarmacadam. I couldn't find the courage to go across and tell him.

On the way home I remembered a television programme I'd seen about flowers buried in the desert which hibernate for years waiting to burst through their whole life cycle during a single day of rain. I felt strong again, like a young bird about to take flight. And I realized why I'd never touched the quarter-acre of garden where all my childhood memories were buried under bamboo stalks of nettles and clumps of weeds. I had been trying to hold up time, to live on in the past having no future to put in its place.

But now the anticipation of change raced in my bloodstream and I wanted to be rid of that shadow. I returned to the silent house where the stained oilcloth on the table, the flaking paint on the wood, the faded wallpaper in the bedroom which light never entered till evening all seemed to be mocking me, reducing me to the child I'd always been. I took the bailing hook from the shed, donned my father's old boots, and as I worked every blow was like an act of finality, a foretaste of the separations to come.

At five thirty my father walked down to the hedge. I still had the letter in my pocket. *Your tea son*, he said, and I shook my head. He watched me work on for a few moments then turned. I swung fiercely at the last bushes until I stopped, my blood calmed in the afterglow of labour. As darkness fell I lit a cigarette among the ghosts of hen-runs and alder bushes and watched the lit windows of the house occluded by the overgrown lilac I hadn't the heart to touch. I felt severed finally from the life of that terrace where I had been delivered, red and sickly, by a country midwife. The bonfire of branches and old timber that I had dosed with paraffin and lit was smouldering. I remember a flatness about the evening as if the whole street had been becalmed in time and then, with a swift flapping of wings, a formation of returning swallows swooped over the rooftops and wheeled upwards in a V across the gardens and out into the distance. And when I looked down, the rotten timbers of the hen house had caught and the carnage began. The shorn surface of the garden looked like a nightmare landscape, fragments lit up and snatched away by the flickering light. Straight black smoke rose to be dissipated into a swirling pall. I watched my childhood burn, the debris of those years borne off into the sky, my final links with what had been home disintegrating into bright quivers of ash.

I'd no idea what lay ahead, all I knew was that as soon as I got my first pay packet I would start the search for a new home, for my own life to begin. I took the letter from my pocket and walked in.

The Wind Beyond the Wall

JOAN MCBREEN

The wind beyond the high wall
at the back of our house
contained itself there,
when barefoot, on the cold bedroom floor
I pressed my face against the glass.

Curtains billowed back created
swaying shadows in the small room.
The night was another world
and I was safe, apart
from the wind beyond the wall.

The lamp before the Sacred Heart glowed,
coals hissed in the grate
and on days missed from school
the hands of the clock on the mantelpiece
seemed scarcely to move at all.

On the small round table
she set cups, plates, new bread.
Mice scuttled in the skirting
when she softly dusted the photograph
of the man in uniform.

In dreams I see his face, recognize
his penetrating gaze
and she and I are back in that house
wanting something beyond
my touch, beyond hers.

On Hearing My Daughter Play 'The Swan'

JOAN MCBREEN

My daughter plays Saint-Saëns. It is evening
and spring. Suddenly I am outside
a half-opened door. I am six years old
but I already know there's a kind
of music that can destroy.

My mother is playing a waltz, Chopin,
and everything is possible. There are lilacs
in a vase on the hall table, white among
the colourful umbrellas, folded,
full of the morning's light rain.

My sisters' voices are calling one another
far down the street. There are wind-blown leaves
under my father's feet as he enters the room.
I look at him as if for the first time
and he grows old.

I see my mother rise from the piano
and close it gently. She takes a glass
from the table. It is empty. But she has put
a weight in me, the weight of something
that has died in her.

As my daughter sustains the melody
with her right hand, the tumult
of the chords she uses with her left hand
brings into the room
the hush and roar of the sea.

25

The Irish Worker

HUGO HAMILTON

The rattling stopped. The wind gathered again to renew its attack on the window. It seemed to gather in the trees and over the houses and possibly around the spire of St Paul's Church. It gathered and sometimes ignored my window completely only to come back with surprise and stronger gusts. The window rattled again, knocked back and forth in its wooden frame. It had no pattern. Sometimes the wind had so much force that it held the window firm under its pressure. Then you could hear the whistle and wheezing more clearly. It was an urgent sound. Only when the gust slackened its resolve again did the window renew its irregular, random banging.

My earliest theory about storms as a boy was that they were caused by giants blowing at each other. That was when I was four. Occasionally, my mother gets out the old school essay to show it to me. Big, freestanding letters from the alphabet. She says I haven't written anything like it since. I haven't replaced the theory either. All I can think of is the constant rattling. It keeps me awake.

I would love to know everything there is to know about wind motion. Set up detailed charts and observations about squalls, gusts, gales and even the smallest buffeting. I'd love to know things that could never be contradicted. Perhaps you could study the wind by colouring it, the same as you could observe a pink liquid curling around in a glass of water or milk clouding in tea. You get an idea how wind moves by watching my father burning leaves and weeds in the garden. It catches the smoke and sends it creeping along the garden wall and then suddenly up straight over the wall where it disperses quickly. Other times, you could watch the smoke seeping up for ages through the moist leaves and drifting down the garden from you and then the wind suddenly blows back and the thick smoke stings you eyes. If it didn't dissipate so quickly, smoke would tell you a lot about wind really. Clouds are too bulky.

The relentless gusts rattling the window tell me nothing. They're too erratic. Finally they propel me out of the bed and over to my desk. I tear up a foolscap page and fold it over and over until it becomes the size of a fat stamp. I tear up another sheet and do the same. I stand there in the bottoms of my pyjamas with the light on. Instead of theory I have practical answers. The thick, folded foolscap pages fit neatly between the frame and the window. Under the blankets again, I listen to the hush.

Outside, new chestfuls and cheekfuls of gathered wind blow against the window. But the window is still. Now I have the impression that something will break. Another heaving force pushes against the window, almost bending the glass. Perhaps I should have left some room to manoeuvre. Taut substance is more brittle. But then I fall asleep and the subconscious gale blows itself out.

When my father went out to work the next morning he found broken slates on the doorstep. He took it almost as a personal affront. That was a dreadful storm last night. The wind almost had a malicious nature. He could have been walking out the door that very moment. The way I got the story, filtering through the half-dream as I got dressed, he might have been killed. That kind of thing is very dangerous.

My mother repeated the words after him as she went to look at the damage. It sounded much more dangerous coming from her in German.

'Das kann enorm gefährlich sein,' she said, seeing the broken slates. It could have sliced someone in the neck. Or it could have chopped someone's shoulder. Or imagine if somebody got that on his head.

'Jemand konnte das auf den Kopf kriegen.' *Jemand*, somebody. The only person going out at that time was my father. Besides, the slates had fallen during the night. The morning was calm and seemed to promise a summer's day. There was no danger. The damage began to reduce from what seemed like three or four slates at first down to one grey slate broken into many pieces.

You couldn't leave a thing like that, even for a day. My father came back in and phoned Mr McNally. He wanted it fixed immediately. He could have phoned him from the office. But there was no time to waste in a situation like that. And Mr McNally, taking it to be a major job, agreed to set everything else aside.

My father was reassured. He picked up his briefcase containing the flask and the sandwiches, the two or three library books, and his copy of the *Irish Press* and set off to catch the train. Before he departed, he left my mother with a final command not to let the children out or at least to make sure they didn't stand under the falling slates.

By the time Mr McNally arrived, I had already had my breakfast and was at my desk in my room. I was studying for the Leaving Cert. It wasn't so much the act of pertinent study. It was more like trying to reduce the feeling of wasted months and wasted years. Hours or even minutes spent away from the books produced guilt and panic. The hounding force of Christian Brothers kept me in my room. There wasn't a minute to waste.

Mr McNally was talking to my mother in the hall. Coming from Kempen in Germany, my mother always had a healthy distrust of Irish workers. She was gentle and discreet. She knew the moods and mind-games that predicted the results. She understood the code under which Irish people worked. It was the spirit of 1916 which burned inside each person still. Her own husband was a fervent Nationalist. She knew that her German accent commanded respect. Her naïve and innocent enquiries got the work done. But you had to watch them, she always said.

'Scharf aufpassen,' are her words. Sharp is a great word in any language. My mother is very sharp when it comes to work.

Mr McNally was no exception. He fixed the roofs on a lot of the houses in Spencer Villas. Whether he was recommended or just happened to be in the right place at the right time was never clear. He didn't have a bad reputation anyway. Mrs Tarleton, the small Protestant woman next door in No. 1, occasionally asked Mr McNally to do the roof for her too. But she didn't trust him any more than my mother did. She used to follow Mr McNally up on to the roof to inspect his work personally. She was seventy, stooped and had bow legs. Mrs Tarleton trusted nobody. Not even us next door. Least of all us in No. 2.

Mr McNally always came and went and worked in the same grey suit. Grey as slate, I suppose. A thin man with a broad forehead. His hair must have been curly once because it now clung tightly to his head like a silver, corrugated bathing cap.

He always reminded me of President Nixon. He was a bit older than Nixon but a lot of the caricatures in magazines and newspapers fitted him just as well. Except that Mr McNally had a more honest face. He didn't look cunning. But then Nixon didn't look cunning until the truth was out.

My mother treated an innocent face with great caution, but what she viewed with even more unqualified distrust was any hint of charm. A man with charm must have something to hide. A man with charm is up to something. Charm and innocence have always been incriminating traits and never worked on her. Mr McNally, as a person, was not without charm either.

'Good morning. Isn't it a magnificent day today?' My mother accepted it as a fact with a long 'Yes, it is.' 'Would you believe it, after such a storm last night?' he added. 'There's a lot of slates down this morning, I can tell you. Well, I suppose I better go up and make sure your roof stays on,' he said with a short laugh as he climbed the stairs in front of her.

To get to the roof, you had to go through a skylight into the attic and straight on through another skylight. It was awkward because you had to stand on the ladder and push the first skylight aside with both hands. I was called to help Mr McNally set up the ladder. He secured it against the banisters with a worn piece of nautical string. My mother was standing by. Her presence, if not providing an eager incentive to work, dispelled at least any observed intention to idle or waste time. As soon as Mr McNally had pushed aside the heavy skylight, she sent me back to my books. 'Mr McNally can manage on his own now.' 'Absolutely,' he replied, looking down the ladder. 'I know these houses like the back of my hand.'

I was in the same boat as Mr McNally. With no further cause to deviate, I returned to my room. He disappeared too after two or three trips up and down the ladder. He explained what had to be done and my mother went downstairs to leave him to it.

Apart from suspicion, one of the sharpest weapons my mother

always had was her highly developed sense of smell. Her nose was very sensitive and she was quite proud of it. We knew it well, even if Mr McNally didn't. I can smell trouble, she would say. I can smell mischief. When we were young, we never doubted the unnatural powers of her fine, long nose.

Suspicion was her way of maintaining order in a large family. Whenever something was up she would look into your eyes and suspect a whole list of crimes to which you answered no each time until she suspected the right one. The silence would confirm it. And you could never tell a lie in a situation like that because she could smell a lie.

One day, when I had stolen a bar of chocolate in Hanahoe's shop, I was almost proud of myself underneath the guilt and terror. I knew I hadn't been seen. There was never any supervision in Hanahoe's. But you could never hide anything in the house so I put the chocolate under a bucket in the garden. I was too tense to eat any of it. When I met her in the kitchen, she knelt down to my level on her hunkers. She asked me straight out if I had stolen something. She couldn't have known. But all I could do was to stare down at her long straight nose and at her two rounded knees and admit. From there on, I had learned an eternal respect for that intelligent faculty of smell. When we grew older, of course, we realized that if you were accused of something you hadn't done, she was bluffing, and you might get away with a white lie. But never where it mattered. Even still, sometimes she appears unexpectedly at the door of my room.

The houses in Spencer Villas are terraced, red-brick houses with Georgian-type fanlights and bay windows to the front. The roofs are all connected from Nos. 1 to 15. This was one of the things that gave rise to the strongest suspicion with my mother. The fact that Mr McNally mended the roofs for other neighbours on the terrace meant that he could easily go up through our skylight and do somebody else's work at the same time.

In fact, she strongly suspected that Mr McNally was also doing a job for Mrs Tarleton next door. He could easily be using good slates from our roof to mend other jobs. But anything beyond the ladder and the skylight remained a collection of notions and suspicions in her imagination. Unlike Mrs Tarleton, she had never actually been up there herself.

My older brother and I knew far more about it. We had been up there a few times and knew the landscape well. Two Toblerone-shaped grey roofs stretched all the way down to the end. They were marked into sections by chimney stacks. In between was the part they called the valley. On a few occasions, we walked all the way along the valley right down to No. 15. With the chimneys at the end of each house, we were able to keep count, calling out the names on the way: Ryans, Richardsons, Beakys all the way down to Beddys. Over the front hump, if you climbed up from the valley, you could see the other side of the street, and the wider, vertiginous view of the bay and of Howth. Over the back, you saw the gardens, trees and surrounding hills. It was an ethereal place. Like being on top of a mountain.

After an hour or so, my mother came up the stairs and stopped at the bottom of the ladder. She called up the ladder to Mr McNally and said she had a cup of tea ready for him. It was the only excuse she had and the only way she could monitor the progress of his work. The risk of allowing deception to carry on unnoticed far outweighed the risk of good work briefly interrupted.

'Mr McNally,' she called again. But there was no response. She waited for an appropriate minute or two to see if he heard her. She waited long enough to dispel any hint of impatience. Then she called again. In the outlines of her German accent, his name sounded more like Mr McNelly.

'Mr McNelly,' she called up through the skylight. Again she paused, so as not to be discourteous.

'Mr McNelly, I have a cup of tea ready for you.' The word 'tea' had emphasis.

There was no reaction. She called a few more times at long intervals and then gave it up. She deduced that he must have climbed out of the valley, out of earshot, on to the outer slopes of the roof. Dangerous place. He was obviously busy. So she went downstairs again and left him alone.

She left it for another half an hour before she came back up again. Once more she stood at the bottom of the ladder, wishing that her fears would only allow her to climb up through the skylight herself.

'Mr McNelly,' she called and then waited to see if he would appear.

A strong beam of sunshine came down through the skylight, making her wince as she looked up. The sun shone through my window as well, projecting a thin, disfigured frame on to the floor of the room. It was a liquid beam full of floating particles.

'Mr McNelly, I have your tea ready now.' She waited quietly. She called twice more but there was no answer. Perhaps his hearing wasn't so good. Perhaps he was still on the outer slopes of the roof. Her calls abated and she went back downstairs again. A little while later I heard her calling from outside in the back garden.

'Mr McNelly.' I heard it clearly through the window. Surely Mr McNally had heard it too? She walked right down to the end of the garden and looked up to see if she could spot him. She called again from there. Allowing that reasonable gap for response, she went back inside. The back door closed with a familiar clap.

She walked through the hallway to the front door and opened it.

'Mr McNelly,' she called from the front garden this time. The name and her accent echoed along the terrace. Then I heard her calling him again, but more faintly than before; perhaps from out on the street or the pavement. A slight breeze began to rush through the house. It rushed and sucked the skylight right down to the front door. It rushed lightly down along the beam of sunlight, down the stairs, through the hallway and, catching the door gently, slammed it shut.

Moments later the doorbell rang and I went down to let her in. She said she was sorry to have taken me away from my study. She explained her difficulty locating Mr McNally. I suggested that he was probably working on something and that he might be best left to it. I went back to my room. She went back into the kitchen.

But very soon she was back up again and once again calling Mr McNally through the skylight. It seemed as though she was calling a celestial spirit. Under the bright beam of sunshine, shielding her eyes, her appellation seemed to be directed at the Almighty.

'Mr McNelly . . . Mr McNelly.' But nothing worked. Her prayers went unheeded and nobody appeared in the skylight.

Eventually she called me instead and asked me to go up the ladder and take a look. She said she was worried that something might have happened to Mr McNally. He wasn't that young either.

Of course I was very happy to be given a decent reason to escape from study but I was less happy to be the instrument of her suspicion. I knew very well that she wanted to catch him out. I asked her if it was not better to leave him up there until he finished his work. I told her if he didn't do his job properly she didn't have to pay him. But that was all irrelevant. She said she was concerned about him.

She insisted. I climbed the ladder along the sunbeam towards the skylight. I was very reluctant to be seen as an inspector—the sting of her suspicion emerging through the skylight. No matter how much she claimed to understand the Irish worker, I claimed to know him better. The one thing he really hates is to be checked up on.

It was very hot on the roof. I was blinded with the sunshine and saw nothing at first. I searched the slopes and saw the shape of Mr McNally, lying back at an angle of 45 degrees against the roof, asleep with his hands behind his head. He must have been two or three houses down from ours. I coughed and he woke up, looking all around him. Then he saw me and got up to walk towards me, dusting himself off.

'Ah, there you are,' he said, almost in chant. 'All finished now.'

Acts of God

CATHERINE PHIL MACCARTHY

When thunder crashed
on the roof

like heavy furniture
I felt the way blind

downstairs in the dark,
found everyone

round the table in the kitchen.
Counting seconds.

Lightning lit the tap
cracked the floor like a whip

made me jump out of my skin.
The unconcerned outline

of my father's shoulders,
my mother somewhere

foraging for matches,
the pitch of my sisters'

voices, our baby upstairs
sleeping, small things

that hold us. Then in the hush,
a downpour.

Under My Skin

CATHERINE PHIL MACCARTHY

In the school holidays
you wrote to me. Described
the amber and purple of sunset
as if I was there with you.

I grew up in the country.
Never knew what to write back,
as if no words could name loss
or how we told the weather

from our gate by the Galtees.
Blue as the faded ink of the Himalayas
for cutting a meadow,
slopes green and close meant rain.

Seagulls feeding in the old garden,
a storm over the Shannon.
At night the moon was a lantern
in the backyard when my father

went out to check cattle.
Dark nights, he searched under the stairs
for the good lamp, pitched bad cess
to blackness. I pressed

wildflowers to the page I sent you.
Your colours stayed with me.
Those landscapes are
the earth under my skin.

Sunlight

FROM MOSSBAWN: TWO POEMS IN DEDICATION

For Mary Heaney

SEAMUS HEANEY

There was a sunlit absence.
The helmeted pump in the yard
heated its iron,
water honeyed

in the slung bucket
and the sun stood
like a griddle cooling
against the wall

of each long afternoon.
So, her hands scuffled
over the bakeboard,
the reddening stove

sent its plaque of heat
against her where she stood
in a floury apron
by the window.

Now she dusts the board
with a goose's wing,
now sits, broad-lapped,
with whitened nails

and measling shins:
here is a space

again, the scone rising
to the tick of two clocks.

And here is love
like a tinsmith's scoop
sunk past its gleam
in the meal-bin.

Home

VONA GROARKE

I always thought this house would hold us;
what we left would stay here, undisturbed,
except to be explained as stories told
of changes that we made to what we found.

In details like the worn upholstery, a cracked door-frame,
the bathroom wall with all our heights marked in,
I found the proof that something would survive
of years lived here, and that in finding it—

on a Sunday visit, or a Christmas stay—
we might come upon a store of memory
that would remind us, call us to ourselves.

I always thought this house would keep us safe,
as when, running from the car
to the front door, late at night,
I knew it was where darkness could not reach.

The dark can make no difference here.
Our house has been blown open
to a vacant future, bleak as January,

in which no window is lit
against the dust and disregard,
where the only sound is the rooks in the chimney,

and the wind sifted through the hall,
closing, opening the kitchen door.

At Every Window a Different Season

MARY DORCEY

I remember a house
where we sat to watch
the days pass;
hour by hour.
The changing of the light
on mountain and lake.
The year's passage
in an afternoon.
At every window
a different season.

Bog and high grass
climbed the mountains
where sheep lay strewn
like white rocks,
cloud catching in their horns.
There were geese in the boreen,
cows in the hedgerows.
A church spire
and the ocean
at the foot of the garden.

On clear nights
stars shimmered
like cut glass
in the immensity of sky
that wrapped itself
and silence
from end to end of the sleeping fields.

In winter
the roar of wind
drowned speech.
Walls shook and timber.
Wave upon wave
rocked our bed,
a curragh at anchor
on the open sea.

I remember
a half door
thrown wide upon waking.
Hay stacks on the front lawn.
In summer
wild flowers rampant;
iris, primrose, foxglove.
And in the pools of sunshine after rain,
a table and chairs
of wrought iron
set out for late breakfast.

A garden adrift
between mist
and heat haze.
Palm trees,
fuchsia,
mallow.
And the wandering pathways
that led to the sea,
paved with orange flags
we carried stone by stone
from the most westerly strand
in the western world.

A house
full of cats and cooking.

Hanging baskets from the rafters;
plants in the baskets
and cats in the rafters
or sun bathing
under wide shaded pottery lamps.
A sailor's hammock,
a hearth and crane,
armchairs drawn to the fire.
Coffee on the stove,
wine on the table.
Music at three o'clock in the morning.

I remember a house
where we sat
to watch the days pass
hour by hour.
The changing of the light
over mountain and lake.
The passage of a year
in an afternoon.
At every window
a different season.

PART 2

Built on Our Embrace

A Ballad of Home

EAVAN BOLAND

How we kissed
in our half-built house!
It was slightly timbered,
a bit bricked, on stilts

and we were newly married.
We drove out at dusk
and picked our way to safety
through flint and grit and brick.

Like water through a porthole,
the sky poured in.
We sat on one step
making estimations

and hugged until the watchman
called and cursed and swung
his waterproof torch
into our calculations.

Ten years on:
you wouldn't find now
an inch of spare ground.
Children in their cots,

books, a cat, plants
strain the walls' patience
and the last ounce of space.
And still every night

it all seems so sound.
But love why wouldn't it?
This house is built on our embrace
and there are worse foundations.

We Are Living

BRENDAN KENNELLY

What is this room
But the moments we have lived in it?
When all due has been paid
To gods of wood and stone
And recognition has been made
Of those who'll breathe here when we are gone
Does it not take its worth from us
Who made it because we were here?

Your words are the only furniture I can remember
Your body the book that told me most.
If this room has a ghost
It will be your laughter in the frank dark
Revealing the world as a room
Loved only for those moments when
We touched the purely human.

I could give water now to thirsty plants,
Dig up the floorboards, the foundation,
Study the worm's confidence,
Challenge his omnipotence
Because my blind eyes have seen through walls
That make safe prisons of the days.

We are living
In ceiling, floor and windows,
We are given to where we have been.
This white door will always open
On what our hands have touched,
Our eyes have seen.

Jock's Holm

MEDBH MCGUCKIAN

I drove along the beach. Not on to the beach. It is mostly a desecration, cars on a beach. Except once when a man had driven his very aged mother down to look at the waves head on, when there was no way she could have walked so far to be so close.

My house was being built at the end of the beach. The two-roomed cottage was being extended into the garden. Walking on one's own earth, it was as if they had let a grave into the ground. The children stared into the square heaps of soil where water seeped where they would be living. When they poured in the concrete it was as Mimi Houghton hinted of the death of Sammy Davis Junior, they are feeding in the morphine now. I thought feeding was strange, considering the wildly natural death of Rilke. Now you can stand on a low wall flattened and imagine a field, or against the horizon a view of it without oneself inside the room that is not yet a floor, the door beyond that is so far only air.

The house grew, its brain began, its grey matter formed meaning. It took something and gave something back, added and subtracted. Like the special beach that is there only one hour one day but every year of one life. Now it rained into the open rafters and golf clubs lay at the windowless windows. It was at least the most easily beautiful place on earth, but I turned left at the bridge and followed the river up into the glen, where the road twisted up the side of the mountain to where my father was born, and along the bed of the valley to where his father had been born. In the end after forest both roads rejoined. I took my grandfather's road which was my great grandfather's road. I passed my great-aunt's cottage which strangers were renovating, as we were. Where she stood cutting her blackberry hedge. Then the main family homestead, the old ruined cottage, the new farmhouse, the newer bungalow, the fresh built barn.

Then into the sacred wood. I drove beyond it first in order to relive it driving back. Past the sheep-fank where we parked the Zodiac and the Humber Hawk and I learned to reverse. Or sat playing Radio Caroline, to Roger Casement's ghost. The haws were Christmas bright. The old pre-fab from Castlereagh my father took apart twice nail by nail and rebuilt twice was still standing, as much as my house in the making. How many dark winter evenings after his teaching day his tired legs had climbed up and down the ladder, his hands reached for his toolbox. Rats and gypsies and cows had trodden where curtains blew and we played gin rummy at the round table on bus-seats. Smoke rose from the new house on the mountain road opposite where he had been born. The big meadow circled round, the sun began on one side and ended on the other. He had cut steps into the bank and carpentered a tap from the stream. The gate fell open but his brother would not disturb these dwellings, even though it was home now only to the cattle. My father only once offered to correct one of my poems. To point out gently a spelling mistake in a word. 'Jock's Home', I had written of a smallish field between here and the hill farm, which should he said be 'Jock's Holm'. I had been led astray by the sound of the Old English.

Cush

COLM TÓIBÍN

Eamon Redmond stood at the window looking down at the river which was deep brown after days of rain. He watched the colour, the mixture of mud and water, and the small currents and pockets of movement within the flow. It was a Friday morning at the end of July; the traffic was heavy on the quays. Later, when the court had finished its sitting he would come back and look out once more at the watery grey light over the houses across the river and wait for the stillness, when the cars and lorries had disappeared and Dublin was quiet.

He relished that walk through the Four Courts when the building was almost closed and everyone had gone and his car was the last in the judges' car park, that walk along the top corridor and down the centre stairway; old stone, old wood, old echoes. He loved the privacy of it; his solitary presence in the vast public building whose function was over and done with for the day.

Years back he would stop for a moment, as he had been instructed to do, and examine his car before he opened the door. Even though the car park was guarded, it would be easy to pack explosives underneath; often as he turned the ignition he was conscious that in one second the whole car could go, a ball of flame. He laughed to himself at the phrase as he stood at the window. A ball of flame. Now things were safer; things were calm in the south.

He went over to his desk and sifted through his papers to make sure that everything was in order for the court. He noticed, as he flicked through the pages of his judgment, that the handwriting, especially when he wrote something quickly, had become exactly the same as his father's, a set of round squiggles, indecipherable to most others.

He gathered the papers together when his tipstaff told him that it was time.

'I'm ready when you are,' he said as though the tipstaff were the one in charge. He put on his robe and his wig, pushing back some wisps of hair before walking out into the broad light of the corridor.

He had learned over the years not to look at anyone as he walked from his rooms to the court, not to offer greetings to a colleague, or nod at a barrister. He kept his eyes fixed on a point in the distance. He walked slowly, with determination. Downstairs, the Round Hall was full, like an old-fashioned marketplace. The corridors were busy as he walked towards the ante-chamber to his court.

This was the last day of term, he would have to deal with urgent business before getting down to read the judgment he had been working on for several months. He looked again through the pages, which had been cleanly typed by a court secretary and then covered by emendations. All the references to previous judgments were underlined, with the dates they had appeared in the Irish Reports in parentheses. This judgment, too, would appear in the Irish Reports and would be cited when the rights of the citizen to state services were being discussed in the future, such as the right to attend a hospital, the right to attend a school, or, in this case, the right to full-time and comprehensive psychiatric care.

He waited in the ante-room. It was still not time. He felt excited at the prospect of getting away. Soon, he would be twenty-five years on the bench and he remembered this last day's waiting more vividly than the humdrum days or the significant or difficult cases, this waiting on the last day of term, knowing that Carmel had everything packed and ready to go.

They spent each summer recess on the coast, close to where they had been born, where they were known. He had been brought there as a baby during the first summer after his mother died. He had spent each subsequent summer there as a child with his father. He thought about it now in the minutes before the court sitting . . .

When he was back in his chambers he telephoned Carmel.

'I have everything ready,' she said.

'It will take me a while. I'll see you as soon as I can,' he replied. He put the receiver down and went again to the window. He watched the small, soft delineations between layers of cloud over the opposite buildings, the strange, pale glow through the film of mist and haze. Suddenly, he had no desire to go. He wanted to stand at the window and clear his mind of the day, without the pressure of the journey south to Cush on the Wexford coast.

The murky heat of the day would settle now into a warm evening in Cush, the moths flitting against the lightshades, and the beam from the lighthouse at Tuskar Rock, powerful in the dense night, swirling around in the dark.

He went back to his desk and thought about it: the short strand at the bottom of the cliff, the red marl clay, the slow curve of the coastline going south to Ballyconnigar, Ballyvaloo, Curracloe, Raven's Point and beyond them to the sloblands and Wexford town.

He stood up and wondered if he had anything more to do; his desk was untidy, but he could leave it like that. He was free to go now; he went over to the bookcases to see if there was anything he should take with him. He idled there, taking down a few books, flicking through them and then putting them back again. He returned to the window and looked at the traffic, which was still heavy on the quays, but he decided he would drive home now, pack up the car and set out.

He drove along Christchurch Place and turned right into Werburgh Street. It had begun to rain, although the day was still bright and warm. He hated days like this, when you could never tell whether the rain would come or not, but this, in the end, was what he remembered most about Cush; watching the sky over the sea, searching for a sign that it would brighten up, sitting there in the long afternoons as shower followed shower.

He had known the house all his life: the Cullens had lived there until the Land Commission gave them a better holding outside Enniscorthy. Himself and his father had gone there as paying guests every summer, and each of the daughters had been what he imagined his mother would have been had she not died when he was born. He remembered each of their faces smiling at him, the wide sweep of their summer dresses as they picked him up, each of them different in their colouring and hairstyle, in the lives they went on to live. In his memory, they remained full of warmth, he could not remember them being serious or cross.

He turned off Sandford Road and pulled up outside the house. He left the keys in the ignition as he went in. The rain had stopped now and the sun was out. He found Carmel sitting in the conservatory at the back of the house with the door open on to the garden. She was wearing a summer dress.

'What's wrong?' he asked. She said nothing, but held his look. Her expression was rigid, frozen.

'Are you all right?' he asked.

'I was asleep,' she said. 'I woke when you rang, and then I was so tired I fell asleep again. It must be the summer weather, it's very heavy.'

'Do you feel all right?'

'I feel tired, that's all. Sometimes I hate packing and moving. I dread it. I don't know why.' She put her hand to her head, as though she was in pain. He went to her and put his arms around her.

'Maybe we could take some of the plants down with us. Will there be room for them?' she asked quietly.

'I'll try and find space for them,' he said.

'Sometimes it looks so bare down there, as though the house wasn't ours at all, as though it belonged to someone else.'

He began to pack the car with bags and boxes, and then he carried out her flowering plants and her sweet-smelling lilies and placed them carefully and gently in the boot and the space behind the front seats of the car. 'One quick jolt and they'll be ruined,' he said and smiled.

'Oh, drive carefully, please,' she said. It had begun to rain and a wind rustled through the bushes in the garden. He found an umbrella to give her shelter as they went out to the car, closing the door behind them.

He drove away from the house. They did not speak until they were beyond Shankill.

'There's something I have to tell you,' she said. 'I was going to tell you this morning, but you were too preoccupied. Niamh came over yesterday to say that she's pregnant. She thought that we had noticed on Sunday when she came to dinner, but I didn't notice anyway. Did you notice?'

He did not reply. He looked straight ahead as he drove. Niamh was their only daughter.

'It was the last thing I thought of,' Carmel went on. 'She sounded very cool, but I think she was dreading having to tell me. How could she be so foolish! I couldn't sleep last night thinking about it. I rang Donal but he didn't know either. You'd think she would have told her brother.'

Carmel did not speak again until later when they stopped at the traffic lights in Arklow. The atmosphere in the car was tense with their silence.

'I asked her who the father was. I didn't even know she had a boyfriend. She said she didn't want to talk about the father.'

When he had driven through the town she spoke again.

'She went to England to have an abortion, and she couldn't face it. She was in the hospital and everything; she had paid her money. I told her that we'd do what we could for her, I told her that I was pro-life all the way. I felt so sorry for her. Imagine Niamh having an abortion. So she's going to have the baby and she's going to keep it. Eamon, I wrote her a cheque. But it's a terrible thing to happen, isn't it?'

'When's it due?'

'November,' she said. 'I can't think how I didn't notice.'

He turned left at Gorey and took the road south towards Blackwater.

'Well, what do you think?' she asked.

'It doesn't matter what I think.'

'It's so hard to talk to you sometimes,' she said.

He parked the car in the lane and opened the side gate into the garden, letting Carmel go in ahead of him. He had the key. The house had been aired; there was a fire burning in the living room, which their neighbours had lit for them, but there was still a musty smell. Carmel shivered and went over to sit by the window. Eamon carried in the first of the plants and put them in the glass porch at the front. The damp smell had always been in the house, he thought, no amount of air or heat would ever get rid of it fully. And there was another smell too which he remembered now: a smell of summer dresses, a female smell. The women who had taken care of him here. He could almost smell them now, vague hints of their presence, their strong lives, their voices which had been heard in this house for so many years.

The nettles had come back into the garden, despite the weed-killer which had been put down in the spring. The nettles seemed taller than ever this year. He would get one of the Carrolls to put the front garden right. Then there would be a new smell of cropped grass, fresh and sweet with a hint of dampness.

He carried the suitcases and boxes in from the car. By now, Carmel had placed her plants all over the house and was in the kitchen. He went over and smelled the lilies which she had put in the porch. He set up the record player and placed the two speakers at opposite ends of the room. He plugged it in, put on a record and turned the sound up and listened to the music as he unpacked the cases and cleared out the car.

They were close to the soft edge of the cliff, the damp, marly soil which was eaten away each year. He listened for the sound of the sea, but heard nothing except the rooks in a nearby field and the sound of a tractor in the distance, and coming from the house the swells of the music. He rested against the windowsill and looked at the fading light, the dark clouds of evening over the sea. The grass was wet now with a heavy dew, but the air was still as though the day had been held back for a few moments while night approached. He heard Carmel moving in the front room. She wanted everything in its place, the house filled with their things, as soon as they arrived, and he stood up now and ventured in to help her.

Charming Red Brick Residence

JENNIFER JOHNSTON

The house he took me to see the next morning was a charming red brick gentleman's residence in good decorative condition with a gem of a mature garden and a large well-maintained barn.

A red brick gentleman in good condition from a London house agency showed us around.

He flourished and jangled a bunch of keys with the expertise of a prison officer.

'Drawing room.'

He ushered us into a room with long windows, full of blue and green sunstreaked light.

'Central heating.'

He opened and shut a door and we caught a glimpse of a shining boiler.

'And wait till you see the kitchen, Mrs . . . um . . . Glover. Just you wait.'

Quarry-tiled floor and an oil-fired Aga. No expense spared. Hand-made pine fittings and a double sink . . . now quite commonplace, but almost unheard of then.

As we climbed the well-proportioned staircase to have a look at the bedrooms and two bathrooms, one en suite, I spoke my first words.

'Why did the owners feel they had to leave this . . . paradise?'

'Isn't it? Isn't it just? Oh dear me, yes.'

He turned and flashed me a smile.

His teeth were very white. He must have a great dentist, I thought.

'Abroad. The lure of abroad. The youngest child out of school at last. They felt they could move away. Isn't it good to indulge yourself if you can? Yes. I say yes, all the time. They bought a charming place on the Côte d'Azur . . . well, a couple of miles up from the coast actually. Quite unspoiled. The firm managed the whole deal for them. Not me personally, you understand, but we do have a department that deals purely in foreign, mainly Mediterranean properties. Yes. It's all starting to open up.'

He shook the keys and unlocked a door.

'Master bedroom.'

He hurried in ahead of us, opening doors and cupboards, waving his hands at the view from the window.

'Bathroom, as I said, en suite, tiny dressing room, built in. As you see, you could move in straight away. Carpets and curtains are up for offer. Some people prefer to make their own decisions about such things and then some people, yes, quite a number really like the no problems ease of just taking what is already in place. Yes.'

He caught Martyn's eye.

'Whoever buys it could move straight . . . quite. Charming bathroom, don't you think? I always think the bathroom is almost the most important . . . Bidet. Brass taps. Very good water pressure, I have been told.'

God, I thought, my mother would hate this man.

He turned on a brass tap and water gushed out.

'See. Some people worry about water pressure. This is another no problem area here.'

He tweaked the tap off again.

'Coming from London where you have every amenity.'

'We're not thinking of leaving London and its amenities.'

He looked surprised and opened his mouth to say something, but Martyn forestalled him.

'May I see the barn?'

'Of course, of course. It's in tip-top shape.'

He set off after Martyn.

'We'll leave you to have a look around Mrs . . . um. Open all the cupboards. You are free to explore fully. Ladies have their own point of view. I always find it a good thing to leave the lady on her own for a while . . . And the garden . . .' He called the words back up as he rushed across the hall. 'The garden is a gem. Do step into the garden.'

I watched them from the bedroom window, winding their way across the grass, through the bushes and trees, just starting to come into tiny leaf. They nodded their heads towards each other like

Chinese dolls. They were each wearing cavalry twills and brown tweed jackets. I longed for Martyn to reach out his hand towards the other man and conjure from his nostril or ear half a pound of Cadbury's Milk Tray, or maybe twenty Player's Navy Cut. I could imagine the alarm on the face of the house agent as the white cylinders plopped from his ear hole.

> *Come into the garden Maud,*
> *For the black bat night has flown.*
> *Come into the garden Maud . . .*

My mother's voice was rich and low.

She used to sing on winter evenings when the curtains were pulled tight. Richly she sang and accompanied herself and the sound of the notes flew out from under her firm fingers.

> *And the woodbine spices are wafted abroad,*
> *And the musk of the rose is blown.*

'Maud' was one of my father's favourites, and he would put his book down and listen to her and nod his head in time to the music.

I used to wonder what he was remembering.

His own mother perhaps, also singing in the flickering firelight? The thought of such continuity is very potent.

I had no music in me.

She also used to sing Schubert.

> *Röslein, Röslein, Röslein rot,*
> *Röslein auf der Hei . . . ei . . . de.*

I was all fingers and thumbs when it came to playing the piano.

'You must concentrate when you practise, Stella. Your mind is always a million miles away. You'll never get anywhere if you don't practise.'

She used to put her head round the schoolroom door and scold me.

My brother John could thunder *Für Elise* at breakneck speed, but I could never get the fingering right. I suppose I didn't want to.

My mother always said you could do anything in the world you wanted, if you tried hard enough.

'Application,' she would say and leave me to ponder.

I will have to have a child to whom I can tell these silly things. Sometime or other.

'Star!'

Bird.

> Birds in the high hall garden
> When twilight was falling.

'Star. Star.'

> Maud, Maud, Maud,
> Were crying and calling.

'Wake up, Star.'

He was below me on the lawn, crying and calling. The house agent, keys in his hand, was standing beside him. Their up-turned faces were pink and expectant. I raised a hand and waved.

A bit like the Queen, I thought.

A gracious wave.

'Come on down, for heaven's sake,' shouted Martyn.

He was rattling coins impatiently in his pocket when I came out of the door.

'What on earth were you doing, standing there like a looney? I shouted and shouted.'

The house agent moved towards me, his face was filled with understanding.

'Having a good sniff round? Yes, of course. I think you'll have found everything A1. Isn't the bathroom suite a peach? I hope you found the linen cupboards in the back landing. Second to none those linen cupboards. Everything to your liking?'

'Yes, thank you.'

'A1. We seldom get a property in such perfect nick as this.'

'The barn is a dream,' said Martyn, taking a leaf from the agent's book.

'I don't doubt it. Well? What's next on the agenda? What other little surprise have you got in store for me?'

The house agent looked alarmed.

Martyn laughed.

'Don't pay any attention to her,' he said. 'Let's go and have a drink. I'm sure there's a pub somewhere.'

'There is. Yes, there is indeed. In the village, just a stone's throw away.' He looked at me and laughed nervously. 'That is, of course if you're quite good at throwing stones. Charming old hostelry. Charming village really, quite untouched by . . .'

'I think I'd like a drink,' I said.

Epithalamion

MICHAEL LONGLEY

These are the small hours when
Moths by their fatal appetite
That brings them tapping to get in,
Are steered along the night
To where our window catches light.

Who hazard all to be
Where we, the only two it seems,
Inhabit so delightfully
A room it bursts its seams
And spills on to the lawn in beams,

Such visitors as these
Reflect with eyes like frantic stars
This garden's brightest properties,
Cruising its corridors
Of light above the folded flowers,

Till our vicinity
Is rendered royal by their flight
Towards us, till more silently
The silent stars ignite,
Their aeons dwindling by a night,

And everything seems bent
On robing in this evening you
And me, all dark the element
Our light is earnest to,
All quiet gathered round us who,

When over the embankments
A train that's loudly reprobate
Shoots from silence into silence,
With ease accommodate
Its pandemonium, its freight.

I hold you close because
We have decided dark will be
For ever like this and because,
My love, already
The dark is growing elderly.

With dawn upon its way,
Punctually and as a rule,
The small hours widening into day,
Our rooms its vestibule
Before it fills all houses full,

We too must hazard all,
Switch off the lamp without a word
For the last of night assembled
Over it and unperturbed
By the moth that lies there littered,

And notice how the trees
Which took on anonymity
Are again in their huge histories
Displayed, that wherever we
Attempt, and as far as we can see,

The flowers everywhere
Are withering, the stars dissolved,
Amalgamated in a glare,
Which last night were revolved
Discreetly round us—and, involved,

The two of us, in these
Which early morning has deformed,
Must hope that in new properties
We'll find a uniform
To know each other truly by, or,

At the least, that these will,
When we rise, be seen with dawn
As remnant yet part raiment still,
Like flags that linger on
The sky when king and queen are gone.

Architecture

MICHAEL LONGLEY

The House on the Seashore
Laying down sand and shingle for the floor
And thatching with seaweed the low boulders
You make an echo-chamber of your home
That magnifies the wind to a cyclone
And keeps you from standing head and shoulders
Above the sea's whisper and the seashore.

The House Shaped like an Egg
Do you pay for this house with egg money
Since its whitewashed walls are clean as shell
And the parlour, scullery, bedrooms oval
To leave no corner for dust or devil
Or the double yolk of heaven and hell
Or days when it rains and turns out sunny?

The House on the Bleach Green
This stump of a tree without any leaves
Can be occupied but never lived in
When snow is lying on the bleach green
And the smallest house you have ever seen
Lets someone inside to watch the linen
From tiny windows with a view of thieves.

The House Made out of Turf
Are the hearth and the chimney built of stone
Or can there be a fireplace for the fire
In a house made out of turf, with its roof
Of kindling, gables that may waterproof
This spacious tinderbox to make a pyre
Of what you built and heated on your own?

New House

MAEVE KELLY

Defying newness I throw down
a carpet, worn, well marked,
and the table in my room
is used, much loved and therefore scarred.

I am careless too of dotty finger pies
on paint gloss and brash skins
of polystyrene, plastic and the like.
A cobweb is a friend crept in,
lured less by old familiar dust
than by the sandstorms left
where woodblock floors are grained
and smoothed in camouflage,
denying age and simpler ancestry.

Last week the mice invaded,
tunnelled through cement,
skipped by open doorways
wore hobnailed boots, as always
when they ranged above the ceiling.
I, being moved to fury
at their crass possession,
shrieked when hand touched one
soft in a drawer of scarves.

Why did I weep, recalling
that old and mildewed house
now making private protest
at southwest gales and mice.

Man on the Doorstep

MACDARA WOODS

He knocks on my door at night
the howling storm made visible
raves at me like conscience
come out he says come out
come out and see the holes in the road
the holes in the road in the rain
it is all falling down around us
holes full of water for children to fall in
and he is right—
five minutes is all it would take
take five to walk to the bottom of the hill
to see these children's graves in the rain

But I can't go out
because I am minding a real live child
I am father to a child
who eats and sleeps and goes to school
flies kites and brings me paintings
and keeps his margins to the edge of the page
or as near as he can at five and a half
who is not for the moment homeless
and depends on me to keep the night outside

Tá Bran ar scoil
Tá Micí ag gáire Tá Lúlú ag gol

No you can't come out says the man
but you can go to bloody Umbria—
and what are you going to do about this
Fascist descent into Anarchism?

What are the artists of Ireland doing?

Safeguard your reputation

I was here this morning in this very place
in this very place today—and
he digs his heel into the crumbling pavement—
and I said to an Indian doctor
an Indian doctor from the College of Surgeons
how can people live in this
in this city falling apart
seeing this same shit day after day and every day
head shaking like John O Gaunt
this same shit and nothing else
enough said said the doctor—

Do you realise
that in the European Parliament
the whole of Europe is laughing at us?
The Germans are laughing at us
the Italians the French
the Greeks and Spaniards are laughing
laughing into their translation machines
laughing like drains
like the rain falling on Dublin they laugh
and the British shoot us

He moves away into the night—
Safeguard your reputation with Cess-Clean
says the advertisement on national radio

Geese and Orchards

DERMOT HEALY

She was eighteen when she married Jonathan Adams. He was forty-three. The day before the marriage he drove down to her home place in the townland of Ballindan, just outside Rathkeale, Co. Limerick. Accompanying him was Matti Bonner, the Catholic labourer Maisie had taken to the hospital that day.

Some time after he proposed Jonathan bought a small house a few miles outside the village. Their nearest neighbour they discovered was Matti Bonner. Since he'd lost his finger in the winch certain types of work were denied him. Maisie hired him to decorate the old house. Having been born in the Republic, she had no religious qualms about knowing Catholics. But the first thing Jonathan Adams did was lift his Fenian ledger to check to see if his new neighbour's name was in it. It wasn't.

Matti Bonner arrived in his blue overalls and with his toolbox. Maisie came out each evening she could get away and gave him instructions. A timber porch was erected round the back. Trellises were raised. Rooms were painted a mint green. He followed her plans exactly. She supervised the plumbing of the kitchen. He ploughed the garden. Set apple trees. Then one night as she and Jonathan sat in the police car surveying the house she said: 'I think Matti should be your best man.'

'You must be out of your mind.'

'He brought us together,' she said, 'and it was a costly experience for him.'

'It's not our fault he lost his finger.'

'If he hadn't we would not be here.'

'If that man is to be my best man,' said Jonathan, horrified, 'there is not one of my family will attend the wedding.'

'It's only right that he be our witness.'

'They won't come, I tell you.'

'Maybe they didn't intend to from the beginning. I don't think your brother Willy approves of me.'

'Matti is Catholic.'

'I know that. But remember you'll be miles from here. It will all be happening in another part of the world.'

'I dare say.'

'Now go up there to his house and ask him.'

'Now?'

'Yes, right now.'

Jonathan pulled back the gate and tapped on Matti's door. The labourer stepped out into the twilight in his vest.

'Sergeant,' he said.

'Matti,' said Jonathan.

They stood there for a few moments. 'Will you come in?'

'Oh, no, no, no,' said the Sergeant. 'I have a question to put to you.'

'Aye?'

'It entails a certain amount of travelling.'

'I see.'

'Well, I can bring you down, but you might have to come home on your own.'

'From where, pray?'

'The county Limerick. You see, I have never been down there,' he said with embarrassment.

'I'd be glad to, Sergeant.'

'Well that's that then. I should add that the woman out there in the car wants you as my best man.'

'She does?' asked Matti in amazement.

They left together the day before the wedding. It was the Sergeant's first time south of the border that he had so astutely protected all those years and suddenly he found himself on collapsing roads that grew narrow, and then narrower. 'Aisy, Sergeant,' said Matti Bonner. Each town was announced by a handball alley and a dance hall. Catholic spires and cathedrals, treeless, flush with Roman excess, sat on the hills while the grey Protestant churches, behind beeches, stood at the end of old-world streets. Gypsy camps, with piles of lead, galvanized sheets and batteries, were scattered on the side of roads. The two men stopped for weak tea, rashers, sausages and eggs in Galway town.

'What do you think, Sergeant?' asked Matti Bonner.

'It's not as bad as I thought.'

Then as they approached Limerick bunting flew overhead.

'They must have been expecting us,' said Matti.

In the centre of the city itself a guard waved them into a parking space. They saw that in every doorway the Holy Family stood.

'You'll have to stop there for a bit, I'm afraid.'

'Is there something wrong?'

'Not a thing.'

Jonathan Adams took stock of the guard's over-sized trousers and dull shoes, the whiskey glint in his eyes.

'Up North,' said Jonathan, 'I might have had that man taken in for questioning.'

'I'll just hop over the road for a minute,' said Matti as they waited. 'I have to relieve myself.'

He disappeared into a pub. Then suddenly a gigantic crowd came round the corner celebrating what a banner called the Solemn Novena. Women, praying in blue, passed in marching lines. The Virgin, also in blue, under a white canopy, was steered down the street. Behind her came a priest flanked by altar boys swishing clouds of incense from thuribles. The priest was reading out the rosary through a microphone, and behind him the others answered, heads back, while thousands of beads moved through their fingers.

When the procession had passed, Matti Bonner climbed back in.

'I took the chance, if you don't mind, to get myself a whiskey,' explained the labourer.

'You can go now,' said the guard, 'just cut across through there and you'll be right as rain for Rathkeale.'

'Thank you, Constable,' said the Sergeant.

'Well, lo and behold you,' the guard replied, 'that's the first time I was ever called that.'

They arrived to Maisie's farm in the late evening. Old Ruttle greeted them on the doorstep. His daughter, he said, would be down in a few moments. A sloe-coloured sky lay behind the house. Dark-nosed swifts were darting round a snug Dutch barn at the back. A timbered porch, like the one Matti had built in Fermanagh, opened onto a garden of beehives. In the distance was another farm, just like Ruttle's, and beyond that another, and another, each similar and each with an orchard. And from everywhere came the honk of geese as they roamed the orchards looking for fallen fruit.

In the kitchen they drank cold lemonade with a ham salad and home-made bread. Maisie shyly made her appearance.

She took them across the fields to meet her neighbours. Matti Bonner was installed with Walter Bovinger, Jonathan Adams in Arthur Teskey's. They met Pamela Gilliard, Gareth Shier, Walter Sparling. Hazel Gardener handed the groom a bouquet of freshly picked flowers. They walked up the disused railway that used to take the American emigrants on to Foyle when the seaplanes were in operation. In the cool dark they sat in a handball alley and kissed.

The morning of his wedding the geese woke him. An argument had broken out among the birds. He watched the males, with necks lowered, begin battle. Then he went below. The Teskeys were squeezing blackberries into white pails in the kitchen. He washed, and Arthur Teskey drove him to the church.

He sat on his empty side one seat ahead of Matti Bonner. The church was bare and dark. The grain in the wooden seats shone. He could smell the Brilliantine from his neighbour's hair. He heard the steps of the Methodists and the Palatines entering the church. 'Good luck, Boss. They're good auld stock,' whispered Matti. Then, from among the other steps, he picked out hers.

Afterwards, if she had let him, he would have driven straight back to Northern Ireland. Instead, she had him drive her through the Ring of Kerry. On to Kinsale, to Wexford, all the places he had never been. She had him promise that he would take her South each year. They drove to Westmeath, then Monaghan, then home.

As her family had done in the South, Maisie set apple trees and fed the apples to the geese she bought at Enniskillen market. Now it was the sound of the geese that started Jonathan Adams' days in the North. She set a herb garden. Cherry trees. Placed flower-sprigged pillows and peach sheets in the visitors' bedrooms. And in their own—white and navy reversible bed linen. In quick succession, when Jonathan Adams was in his late forties, she had two daughters, Catherine, named after Maisie's mother, and Sara.

'They were both conceived in Rathkeale,' she told him.

'It accounts,' he replied, 'for their reluctance to be specific.'

From the beginning he expected a policeman's daughters to be beyond reproach. He took them to school, to Sunday School, to services. One on either hand, he descended the barracks steps. He washed them in the bath together. He was an old man graced by the miracle of young daughters. And the first thing their father did when they had learned to speak was to send them to elocution and drama classes. They learned to balance the sound of a word on their palate before they spoke it. He did not want any child of his to find herself before a congregation or audience stumbling over the meaning of that word 'I'.

They were taught the trumpet and the violin. Maisie made them velvet cushions to place over the chin rests. Their small heads fell sideways behind the bow. A moment's silence while they fretted and grimaced and tried to remember the tune. He brought them to the spring agricultural shows in Enniskillen. Huge brown bulls with white loins stared at them through the railings. Each side of him they stood on Remembrance Days by the monument. They watched the Salvation Army Band and clapped when he clapped.

Each night he read to them from the scriptures. His daughters and his wife became the congregation he had lost that fateful day in Cullybackey. From her father Catherine first heard warnings against the sins of the flesh through the words *lust*, *carnal*, *licentious*. The words swooped from her father's tongue onto hers, words that years later used to send dizzy tremors of desire through Jack Ferris.

'Lust,' Jonathan Adams would say, and the girls could feel it—a surge of feeling that started in the body and entered the spirit like a black wind.

The House of the Architect's Love Story

ANNE ENRIGHT

I used to drink to bring the house down, just because I saw a few cracks in the wall. But Truth is not an earthquake, it is only a crack in the wall and the house might stand for another hundred years.

'Let it come down,' I would say, perhaps a little too loudly. 'Let it come down.' The others knew what I meant alright, but the house stayed still.

I gave all that up. We each have our methods. I am good at interior decoration. I have a gin and tonic before dinner and look at the wallpaper. I am only drunk where it is appropriate. I am only in love where it stays still. This does not mean that I am polite.

Three years ago I hit a nurse in the labour ward, because I had the excuse. I make housewife noises in the dark, to make your skin crawl. I am glad he has given me a child, so I can drown it, to show the fullness of my intent.

I boast, of course.

Of all the different love stories, I chose an architect's love story, with strong columns and calculated lines of stress, a witty doorway and curious steps. In the house of an architect's love story the light is always moving, the air is thick with light. From outside, the house of the architect's love story is a neo-Palladian villa, but inside, there are corners, cellars, attics, toilets, a room full of books with an empty socket in the lamp. There are cubbyholes that smell of wet afternoons. There are vaults, a sacristy, an office with windows set in the floor. There is a sky-blue nursery where the rocking-horse is shaped like a bat and swings from a rail. And in the centre of it all is a bay window where the sun pours in.

It is familiar to us all. At least, it was familiar to me, the first time I walked in, because all my dreams were there, and there were plenty of cracks in the wall.

The first time I didn't sleep with the architect was purely social. We were at a party to celebrate a friend's new extension. There had been connections, before that, of course, we were both part of the same set. If I ever wanted an extension, I would have come to him myself.

I asked him about terracotta tiling and we discussed the word 'grout'. I was annoyed by the faint amusement in his face when I said that white was the only colour for a bathroom sink. 'I am the perfect Architect,' he said, 'I have no personal taste. I only look amused to please my clients, who expect to be in the wrong.' There was a mild regret in his voice for all the cathedrals he should have built and we talked about that for a while.

The second time I didn't sleep with the architect was in my own house. I shouldn't have invited him, but the guilt was very strong. I wanted him to meet my husband and go away quietly, but he spent the time pacing the room, testing the slope of the floor. He knocked on the walls too, to see which were partitions, sniffed slightly in front of my favourite picture and told me the bedroom was a mistake. 'I know what you mean,' I said, and then backed away. I said that I could live in a hole at the side of the road, so long as it was warm. 'Do you ever think of anything?' I asked, 'except dry rot?' We were perfectly at home with one another. Even so, there were many occasions in that first year when we did not make love.

The reasons for this neglect were profound, and not to be confused with an absence of desire. The architect and I had both built our lives with much deliberation. The need to abandon everything, to 'let it come down' had been mislaid long ago. We understood risk too well. We needed it too much. There was also the small matter of my husband and a child.

It is a quiet child with red hair. It is past the boring stage and runs around from room to room, taking up my time. It would be a mistake to say that I loved her. I *am* that child. When she looks at me I feel vicious, the need between us is so complete, and I feel vicious for the world, because it threatens the head that I love. On the other hand, wives that are faithful to their husbands because they are infatuated by their offspring don't make sense to me. One doesn't have sex with one's children.

I am unfaithful with my husband's money—a much more pleasant occupation. My life is awash with plumbers and electricians, and I change all the ashtrays twice a year. I watch women in fitting rooms, the way they stick their lips out and make them ugly when they look into the mirror. I wonder who they are dressing for and I wonder who pays.

My husband earns forty thousand pounds a year and has a company car. This is one of the first things he ever told me. But I fell in love with him anyway.

After I hadn't slept with the architect a few times, I took to riding buses as though they were the subways of New York. I sighed when the air-brakes loosened their sad load, and sat at the front, up-top, where I could drive with no hands. I became addicted to escalators, like a woman in a nervous breakdown. Stairs were for sitting on, with my child in my lap. I joined the local library for that purpose.

These were all things I dreamed about long before I met the architect, which makes this story dishonest in its way. Under excuses for sitting on library steps I could also list: simple fatigue, not winning the lottery, not liking the colour blue. Under excuses for killing babies I could list: not liking babies, not liking myself, or not liking the architect. Take your pick.

I don't mean to sound cold. These are things I have to say slowly, things I have to pace the room for, testing the slope in the floor. So. The architect is called Paul, if you must know. His parents called him Paul because they were the kind of people who couldn't decide on the right wallpaper. Paul has a mind as big as a house, a heart the size of a door and a dick you could hang your hat on. He never married; being too choosy, too hesitant, too mindful of the importance of things.

I wanted to function in and around his breakfast. I wanted to feel panic and weight. There was the usual thing about his smell, and where I wanted that. (I felt his body hard against me. His eyes opened so slowly, I thought he was in pain. 'Oh Sylvia.' His breath was a whisper, a promise against my skin. The green flame of his eye licked my mouth, my neck, my breast.) But I'm sounding cold again. The architect's smell would have spiralled out from me to fill uncountable cubic feet. I loved him.

Not sleeping with the architect helped my marriage quite a bit. I discovered all kinds of corners in my husband, and little gardens in his head. I was immensely aware of how valuable he was as a human being, the presence he held in a room, the goodness with which he had given me his life, his salary and his company car. I was grateful for the fact that he still kissed for hours, as though the cycle of our sex lives was not complete. (Sex with my architect would have been horribly frank, nothing to say and nothing to hide.)

My husband came in to breakfast one morning, and his hands were shaking. He said 'Look what I have done.' He was holding a letter that he had picked up in the hall. 'I tore it up,' he said. 'It was for you, I'm sorry.' He was very bewildered.

If it was wartime, we could have clung to each other and burnt the furniture, we could have deceived the enemy with underground tunnels and built bombs out of sugar.

As it was, I rode the buses and he worked and we loved each other well enough.

The idea of the house grew into our marriage. I don't know who suggested it in the end, but I rang Paul and said, 'Aidan wants you to think about some plans. We want to build. Yes at last. Isn't it exciting?' and my voice echoed down the phone.

I needed this house to contain, to live in his love. It would be difficult of course. There would be a lot of meetings with the door ajar, talking about damp-courses. The arguments over where the walls should be would mean too much. I would listen to the architect's big mind and his big heart and look at his shoes. His voice would ache and retract. The green flame of his eye would lick me quite a bit. All the same, I would not fling my life into his life and say that he owed me something (which he did; which he knew), responsibility being impolite these days, even with parents who gave birth and bled and all the rest. Besides, all he owed me was a fuck and whatever that implied.

I had not slept with the architect seventeen times, incidentally.

I chose the site, a green field as near to a cliff as I could find—something for the house to jump off. We would take risks. From the front it would look like a cottage, but the back would fall downhill, with returns and surprises inside.

Of course he was good at his job. The place rose like an exhalation. The foundations were dug, the bones set, and a skin of brick grew around the rest. It was wired and plastered and plumbed. Much like myself, the first time I slept with the architect.

It was in the finished house. We were walking the empty shell, making plans to fill it in. I was joking most of the time. There would be no banisters on the stairs. The downstairs toilet, I said, should be in Weimar Brown and Gun Metal Grey, with a huge lever set in the floor for the flush. The bathroom proper would have an inside membrane of glass filled with water and fish. The master bedroom would be a deep electric blue, with 'L O V E' like a neon sign hung over the door. *Trompe-l'œil* for the dining room, even though it was no longer the rage, forests and animals, built out of food. I would coat the study walls with dark brown leather and put a cow grazing on the ceiling.

'It's just a house, Sylvia,' he said. 'Quite a nice house, but a house all the same,' as he led me through the flexible, proportioned spaces that he made for me. It was all as familiar to me as my dreams: the kitchen, where we did not make love, with wires and tubes waiting in the walls; the dining room where he did not eat me; the reception room where he did not receive me; the bedrooms where he did not bed me.

I should tell you who made the first move and what was said. I should say how I sat down on the stairs and how his big, hesitant heart cracked under the strain.

So we did it on the first landing and it was frank, comprehensive, *remarkably* exciting and sad. I thought the house might fall down around our ears, but it stayed where it was.

The payment of debts is never happy. All he owed me was a fuck and whatever that implied, which in this case is a child. I loved the architect and the architect loved me. You think that makes a difference.

In my childhood book of saints there were pictures of people standing with ploughshares at their feet, cathedrals in their hands. This is the church that St Catherine built. If I painted myself now there would be a round hazy space where my stomach is, and a cathedral inside. This baby is a gothic masterpiece. I can feel the arches rising up under my ribs, the glorious and complicated space.

I can feel it reaching into the chambers of my heart, and my blood runs to it like children into school. We have the same thoughts.

Historical women killed their children more than we are used to; it was one of the reasons for the welfare state. Killing your child is an 'unnatural act'. As if money were nature and could set it all to rights. Money is not nature. I have plenty of money.

I don't want anything so bland as an abortion. Killing something inside you is not the same, we do that all the time. Don't be shocked. Perhaps I will love it instead. Perhaps I will never find out what is inside and what is outside and what is mine.

We had Paul over for the celebration dinner in our new house, with its avocado bathroom, the bedroom of bluebell white, the buttercup kitchen, the apple-green dining room, and the blue, blue, blue-for-a-boy nursery, with clouds on the wall. I was a beautiful hostess, dewy with pregnancy, surrounded and filled by the men I love. Aidan is a new man. The house, the child, would have saved our marriage, if it needed saving. 'Let it come down,' I say, but the house is inside my head, as well as around it, and so are the cracks in the wall.

Tom

MARY LAVIN

When Mary at last made up her mind to join the young people, in the parlour, they were singing so loudly that for a few minutes they did not notice that she had come into the room, nor see her standing in the doorway.

At the piano there sat a stout young man who was a stranger to her; but she knew all the others.

For all the world as if they were set in motion by some swinging pendulum, they swayed this way and that, in time to the music, while from their open mouths, as fragrance is spilled from a censer, there spilled out song to either side. And on the last note of the song every mouth in the room was as round as a ring, and through the smoke that filled the room the young people exchanged glad eyes. It was a happy scene. Mary stood at the door, and looked in upon them all, but especially her eyes sought and rested on her eldest son. All the others, she could see, were in one way or another touched by the sentiment of the old song. Tom was sad, and the young people stirred by secret longings. Patrick alone was unaffected. Sitting on the arm of a chair, he too was singing, and singing at the top of his voice, while, like them too, he swayed from side to side in time to the music, but if he felt anything at all, it was amusement, even perhaps a little contempt, for the simple taste of the others.

Alice is right, she thought, looking at him. He will not be content with us for much longer. Then, while she was looking at him, Patrick looked across the room and saw her.

'What's the matter, Mother? You look as if you'd buried your whole family.'

The song was at an end. The young man at the piano swung around on the piano stool, and everyone began to make room for Mary. Bart sprang to his feet at once, and wanted her to take his chair.

'Come over here, Mother,' he cried, but his last word was greeted by a peal of laughter.

'Well, what about it?' challenged Bart. 'Everyone else in the family calls her Mother, so I don't see why I shouldn't!'

At this, Ellie blushed furiously, and Angie had to make the retort that modesty demanded.

'Well, you're not one of the family, Bart!' she cried.

But she knew, and everyone else knew, the answer that fitted this like a glove.

Bart looked at Ellie.

'That's not my fault,' he said, and he addressed Mary again. 'Is it, Mother?' he asked.

But at this there was another peal of laughter, and as for Mary, she felt as if something warm had been thrown around her shoulders. How simple they were, all of them; how easily their fun and their happiness sprang up out of nothing.

How can he leave us? her heart cried, for amid the laughter and the teasing, she saw out of the corner of her eye that Patrick was yawning.

But the young man at the piano had dropped his hands upon the keys again.

'Do you know this?' he asked, and before anyone had time to give him an answer, a strong rich baritone, that somehow or other up to this had been smothered in the medley of voices, broke over the room with such strength and beauty that, although everyone present knew the old song word by word, and note for note, no one wanted to do anything but listen. It was the 'Irish Emigrant.'

As if he had taken for granted that they would accompany him, the singer had at first been diffident, but then, finding himself soaring alone, after a line or two his voice took on a greater power and strength.

All their lives, those who listened had been familiar with these words, but so potent was the voice of the singer that it was as if only now for the first time, they were touched by the feeling that underlay the sad and lovely plaint. Slowly, a change had come over the whole room, and whatever about the men, there was not one of the women but whose lips trembled and in whose eyes the tears had not begun to glisten.

The glorious voice rose in a swell, and softly it sank again, and then where only a voice had been, there sat upon the piano stool the slightly rotund figure of the strange young man; but this time no one applauded him. A rich, deeply satisfying silence hung over all. And so silent were the young people in particular they seemed to have been put under a spell.

On the settee, Bart, with unaccustomed seriousness, was looking into Ellie's eyes, and across their heads Willie Haslip looked at Angie with his gentle gaze. Even Patrick's eyes rested with an odd reflective expression upon Alice. But Alice had bent her head.

She's crying, thought Mary, and she wondered if Patrick understood the reason for those tears. She would have liked to watch them, those two young people, but no one had complimented the singer. She turned to him.

'That was a beautiful song,' she said, 'and you have a beautiful voice.'

But her own voice sounded tired, and noticing this, and feeling a lowering of their own energy and vitality after the singing, the visitors became conscious of the lateness of the hour.

'Well, much as I hate to say it, I'm afraid we had better be thinking of the road, Willie,' said Bart, standing up.

Willie was instantly on his feet.

'I was just about to say the same,' he said, and remembering that he had brought no overcoat with him, he began to turn up the collar of his coat. 'I wonder what kind of a night it is?' he said, and he looked at Angie.

'I'll go as far as the door with you,' said Angie at once. 'It may be a nice fine night—' she hesitated a moment— 'like last night,' she said.

'Where were you last night?' There was a sharp note in Willie's voice.

'Nowhere,' said Angie quickly, 'but I was looking out of my window when I went upstairs and I saw it was a bright starry night.'

Their eyes met. A look of shame came into the young man's eyes as if he had been guilty of some enormity, to obtain pardon for which, had they been alone, he would have thrown himself on his knees before her. But here, now, in front of the others, he could only look at her mutely. But perhaps his look was not so mute as it seemed. Perhaps it spoke with a thousand tongues, and received a thousand answers. Or perhaps it asked but one question:

'Will we, one night, look out together upon that starry sky?'

'Well?' It was Bart who broke in upon them. 'Did I hear you say you were coming to see us to the door, Angie? What about you, Ellie?'

Ellie was still sitting on the settee.

'I hate to stand up,' she said, yawning.

But it was so certain that she would do so, and more than that, that she and Angie would go out to the front gate, Mary went ahead of them all out into the hall and took down a coat from the rack.

'Here, Ellie,' she said, holding out the coat to her. 'Here, Angie,' she said, having found another one with some difficulty on the loaded rack. 'Put that on your shoulders. These evenings are getting very chilly. And don't stand many minutes in the cold. You know your father wouldn't like it.'

Tom, at that moment, however, was helping the strange young man into his coat and handing him his hat. Mary looked at them. She had not asked, and had not been told, the name of the visitor. Did Tom know him, she wondered. What does he think about it all, she wondered suddenly, about Bart and Ellie, and about Angie and her young man? And what will he think about Patrick when he hears about him? I suppose he'll just say I can't expect to keep them forever.

If they all left us, he wouldn't mind a bit, she thought. He'd be just as content for us both to be sitting here in the house alone, one on either side of the fire, like we used to sit long ago before any of them were born.

As if things could ever be the same again! Men were so insensitive!

It was hard at times not to feel contempt for them. And indeed there was a slightly contemptuous look on Mary's face as, a few minutes later, having sent Patrick down the street with

Alice, to see her safely to her door, and having warned the girls once more not to stay too long out at the gate in the cold, she and Tom turned back from the door and went together into the kitchen.

'Is the back door locked, Tom?' she asked impatiently. He took care of that for her on most nights of the week, but to-night he had made no effort to help her, but sat down by the dying fire looking into it. She went on with her chores, but more and more as the minutes went by she was aware of him. There was something on his mind.

'Mary?'

She was winding the clock, but she looked up. She knew there had been something troubling him.

As their eyes met, however, he stared at her in a curiously helpless way, a victim to the long habits of a lifetime of inarticulateness. In her heart Mary knew she could help him, as she had done on the few other occasions in their life when he had shown himself to be under stress of wanting to say something out of the ordinary. But to-night she was very tired, and beyond looking at him questioningly, she gave him no help.

For a moment some disturbance, caused by what was in his mind, showed itself upon his homely face, and in his honest, kind eyes, but when she made no effort to go to his assistance, he was unable to put it into words.

'It's after eleven,' he said at last, rising from his chair. 'I don't like the idea of the girls standing outside at the gate at this hour.'

'Is that what you wanted to say to me?' said Mary sarcastically.

'Isn't it something that ought to be said?' he replied, a shade of truculence in his voice, but she knew that he was not annoyed with her, nor indeed with the young people either, but with himself for not having been able to get out what was on his mind. She yawned.

I'll hear it in time, she thought, and giving a last look around the kitchen, she handed him the alarm clock.

'Are you coming up?' she asked, taking up a bundle of Rosie's clothes that had been airing all the evening at the side of the stove.

It was a long time since she had been so sleepy. At the foot of the stairs she yawned again. The young people were delaying a long time. Tom was right, though she would not want him to know that she agreed with him on the point. I won't be able to go to sleep until I hear them come back into the house, she thought, until I hear the door clap home, and the chain rattle into its socket. But as soon as these symbols of safety sounded in her ear, it would not be long until she lost her hold upon the day, and was fast asleep. Not until then, though, not until then; not until they are all safely back in the house, she thought, as she mounted the stairs wearily, and wearily folded back the covers of the bed and began to take off her clothes.

But she must have been more tired than she knew, for when Tom came up the stairs Mary was asleep.

She must have been very tired, he thought, as he stood still in the middle of removing his collar and tie, and listened to her steady breathing, and looked at her sleeping face. She never went to sleep before without waiting to hear the last one of the family come in and bang the door.

There!

Downstairs the hall door was closed with a thud, and one after the other, the different voices of the three young people could be heard as they made their way into the kitchen.

I suppose she wasn't worried when she knew they were only outside the door, he thought, as he put out the light and slipped quietly in by her side.

I'm tired too, he thought. But somehow he didn't go asleep as quickly as usual. He didn't seem inclined to sleep at all.

It was hot. He felt inclined to toss and turn but he was restrained by the thought that he might disturb the peaceful sleeper by his side. Considerate always, to-night a new tenderness, a new anxiety such as he had never felt before in all their life together, took possession of him and as he listened to her breathing, his own breath was almost an agony to him, so desperately did he try to keep it even and gentle. In the darkness it seemed to him that it was stertorous and violent.

It would awaken her. For a time the dread of doing so made his heart beat faster, but as he lay there sleepless, a feeling of loneliness came over him, and there stole into his heart a wayward wish that she would waken.

If she were to waken now, in the darkness, where they were alone together, he would have no difficulty in pouring out all that had welled up within him downstairs when the young people were singing that song. That song, even now he could not get the words of it out of his head. And, as at the time it was sung in the parlour, and afterwards in the kitchen, he was almost overpowered by the flood of tenderness that swept over him. Only now, with no one to see, he did not try to stop the tears that flowed into his eyes. And he wasn't one for tears.

Not once, since he was a little boy, could he remember having shed a tear, although downstairs in the parlour he nearly made a fool of himself before them all. Because for him, Mary and the Mary in the song were one, and his heart had been rent in him while the song lasted. Then, looking up suddenly, he had seen her standing in the doorway.

She was in her prime. Fascinated, he had stared at her, his feelings of pride and joy only comparable to the way he felt the first evening she consented to meet him more than twenty years ago, when she was a young country girl with her hair down her back.

She was a woman now, but a woman in her prime, and there was still about her that curiously country air and manner that marked her out among all the women around about them in the locality. There she was, the mother of a grown-up family, and yet she was so strong and firm and straight, her skin so soft and clear, her cheeks so pink and her eyes so bright and eager. She was a mother five times over, and yet it was only by the softness of her breast and the wisdom in her eyes that this could be known to anyone.

She had borne him five children. Five times she had lain down in the pain of childbirth, here in this very house. How had she risen again so fair and so unbroken by what she had suffered? And more amazing still, how had he endured the torment of waiting, helpless, downstairs until her agony was spent?

What had he felt at those times? Had he not been frantic with fear as she hovered in those dark vales of pain? He tried hard to remember, but in the end he had to face the plain fact that he could not recall what he had felt, or even what he had done during those hours of her pain and anguish.

If he had again to face one of those long days of waiting for her confinement to come to an end, and her delivery to be accomplished, how would he endure it?

This thought had struck him in the parlour, but now in the dark room it came back to him, and with it there came another thought, swifter and more terrifying. What made him think of those days of her fecundity as days that were over and passed? She might even at this moment be carrying within her, unknown to them, another child for whose sake she would once again have to make that terrible journey through the vales of pain.

No: it could not be. He was once more fully awake, but all the same, fear gripped him like a vice, and it seemed to him that only by shouting could he free himself of it. To shout; to scream; to let one loud cry break from him; that only, it seemed, would give him ease. To let one single word tear its way from his strangled lungs: the word No. No! That one word alone would bring him ease if he could but shout it loud enough: loud; loud; loud.

If anything were to happen to her? A cold sweat broke over his face. For it was the first time in their lives together that the thought come to him that one day, sooner or later, they would have to part.

Right from that first day he had seen her sitting in the tram he had felt his heart leap, and ever after he had not been satisfied until he had settled things so that she was going to belong to him forever. But now for the first time he realized the limitations of that word; its earthly boundaries. One day, they must part, and, looking at her form, that he faintly discerned or fancied he could discern, beside him, the frailty and fragility of her sex made him feel uneasy about her. If he should ever lose her! How would he endure one day without her?

A terrible cold feeling had replaced the feverish heat of a moment before. He shuddered. They would one day be separated, and then, not until they lay together under the clay would they be stretched side by side again. He shuddered once more.

He would light the gas, he thought. That might dispel the dark fancies that tormented him.

But he didn't light it. Instead he made an effort to be practical. After all, he was always considered to be a man of good sense.

If only he could get some sleep. Perhaps if he turned over once, gently, he might not disturb her, and he might find it easier to sleep on his other side?

Before he turned, however, he reached out his hand, and gently, lightly, as if they were strolling outdoors in the daylight, he clasped her sleeping hand in his.

PART3

The

Lost Citadel

The Lost Citadel

MARY O'DONNELL

Until today, the only guarantee of escape was to swim. Thea says it's an obsession. Perhaps it is. Either way, every evening at six I drive to the shore and strip to my underpants. If the tide is high, I wade out to the Gull Rock, until waves buoy me in such a way that I am deposited quite gently on the shelf. My back-side has grown accustomed to the abrasions of mussel-shell and limpet.

Then I clamber across to the southernmost tip and prepare to dive. In that moment the sea drowns out everything, receives my pale flesh with its own visceral embrace. Imagine the weight of thoughts that float out of every swimmer into the ocean! How easily we are absorbed by our first element, how becalmed the mind as the body dives!

What I can never fully explain to Thea, is almost inadmissible, even to myself. The sea has always helped. Until today, that is.

I know that by the time I have swum ashore to pat myself dry and unpeel my sodden pants, she will have collected the child from the crèche after work, that as I walk in the door she will in all probability be making him eat his tea, or making him wash his hands. *Making* being the operative word.

So today, it all rushed back, as it does occasionally, a feeling that sparkles like ice or diamonds impaled in me with chill precision. Even though the whole thing happened a year ago. The memory always coincides with conflict of some kind. And besides, we had had a bad row only yesterday. She said I exaggerated, that I over-reacted.

'I—do—not—over-react!' I answered in a staccato voice.

I would rather spoil him, as she would call it, than do the opposite. Much as she wishes it, I will not collude in the strategies of adult tyranny.

'It's not tyranny!' she practically scoffed, 'Someone has to discipline the child, for God's sake, even if you can't!'

'There are other ways. There *are* other ways to—'

'Like what?' she challenged, 'You tell me how we stop him screaming night after bloody night when he knows we're in the house, when there's absolutely *nothing* wrong with him!'

I was helpless to respond. His screams return again and again, circling my skull, jabbing at my stomach.

Today the tide was quiet, viridescent, then as I struck out, the sun spattered the bay between Giant's Crag and the Cove. I might not have ventured in, had I sensed what would occur. The air seemed warmer than on land. Not for the first time, only minutes into my swim, I detected that rank odour. It is distinctive. Smoke. The kind of smoke that wafts from food being cooked in the open, smoke and charred animal flesh.

Thea and I can talk about such things, the unusual, the singular, or the inexplicable. Naturally, she long ago concluded that it was a folk memory, though how a folk memory can strike the olfactory senses is beyond me, even if the old Norman citadel was located right there above the cliffs, even if it was big and bustling and a place for trading.

For a woman of such intuition, she can be harsh where the child is concerned. Dim, dare I say it.

I always looked forward to the prospect of bringing him out with me, of gradually teaching him about water, and about his own strength and weakness. Of course, he's only six. And when I pick up the acrid tang of smoke and flesh on the sea air I wonder, will he ever smell what I smell? And will his eyes come to rest on the cliff face as mine do, probing the crinkled erosions? Will he casually search the tawny excrustations for traces of lost settlements, places where men and boys were joyous and sure of themselves, now buried between the sand-martin's nests and the kittiwake ledges?

Backwards and forwards we go, Thea and I, like contestants in some kind of batting game. Except that one of us doesn't always want to bat ball and the other is all too eager. Every so often she talks about women always being the ones left to do the disciplining and then getting blamed for it.

'You're lily-livered where he's concerned. What're you afraid of?' she goads, the veins in her forehead bulging with anger.

When she comes out with that I grit my teeth. How many domestic crimes are averted through the most rigid self-control, a seizing up of the facial muscles as the weak or inadequate or irresponsible spouse stands accused by an all-too-triumphant partner?

Not for the first time I thought again today of the lies spoken in the name of childhood. That childhood is a time of inviolate growth, that there is peace and discovery and fun. Lies, lies.

This evening, I came into the kitchen wearily. My hands were still cold, unusually so, the fingers tingling with numbness. There he was, struggling with his shoes, which she claims he should by now be able to manage himself. He looked too innocent, too innocent by far, grunting and whining as he forced the left shoe onto his right foot. She could see him too. She sat quite still, feet curled beneath her on the sofa, her nose, as usual, in a book.

I bent to help him. She looked up and sighed.

'Can't you let him be?' she said, not unkindly. 'He has to learn for himself.'

'But we have to show him, Thea.'

'If I've shown him once I've shown him forty times. Can't you see—it's all for *attention*!'

Once more, beaten into a cul-de-sac. He stopped pulling at the shoe, tugged it off again and ran towards me.

What torments me most is the quality of his forgiveness, which seems absolute, and not marred by fear. And yet I wonder at his notes, the scrawled messages delivered to both our pillows in new, shaky writing.

'To Daddy and Mammy, you are good to me.'

Or 'Thank you Daddy and Mammy I love you I will be good.'

I quake at the thoughts of him, I still hear him scream, I still see the little legs kicking out in an attempt at childish defiance which he could not possibly sustain.

And again, again, I ask myself why I did it, why I listened to her?

For a short while today, the sea soothed me. This time I stripped completely standing by the jeep, fired my clothes into the torn passenger seat. Pieces of his Lego set lay on the floor. Complete nakedness felt good. There was nobody around, except for a mooning couple some few hundred yards up towards the sand-bar, too absorbed in one another to notice a pale, greying man.

I was cleansed again, swam eight hundred yards breast-stroke, turned and swam eight hundred more front crawl, turned again and backstroked, my eyes open and my head singing with the sounds of ocean and gull, and the smell of the Norman fires which I now took for granted rushing to my nostrils, and then—at first I wasn't certain—voices. Mens' voices, powerful laughter, which crushed over my body and faded too suddenly, as if washed through with something more sinister.

Then I heard it, as clearly as if Thea and I were in the bed-room, or arguing in front of the child, or at our own hearth with the logs hissing and the coal crackling. Well out of my depth, I stopped swimming and floated, my ears throbbing.

Not even the sea could save me. The current beneath became a shaft of ice, fixing me in a state of solid fear. But it was more than the current, and I continued to float in an attempt to re-cover my equilibrium, told myself that it would be alright, that things would sort themselves out in time, that time was a healer. Yet when the ancient voices faded, all I could hear was one child's voice, the screams and the fear of one child as I tried to please her, doing my best to see things her way. It was the middle of the night. He'd been calling for hours, whinging and sobbing. Finally, it was my turn, and I bore her rage like a ball of steel, grabbing him from beneath the bed-clothes. He roared as I shook him. Then I struck and could not stop. I flailed at his legs and arms with my man's strength, as if to finally quieten him, or show him that this was the way and once and for all, he would behave for her.

'No Daddy! No Daddy! Oh please, no Daddy I'll be good, I will Daddy, oh Daddy!' he wailed and gulped, slipping once from my grasp and running to the bathroom, where I missed him again and he jumped into the bath, screaming, the tears bursting from him, crouching finally, hands over his head as my blows rained down and his forehead struck the tap.

Thea stopped me, her face white and wet.

'Not that much, not that much!' she called, catching my arm . . .

I think I almost drowned this afternoon. Perhaps I wanted to. Or else it was my own weeping, inaudible amidst all that water and salt, a great weight crushing my lungs as I lost my breath and slipped under for those few moments.

I love the smell of him. His skin. His soft hair. His breath, which is always sweet.

There is nothing he cannot—could not—do, given the right chance. There is nothing we could not accomplish, a father and a son. I would die for him.

The Tale of the Cottage

EMMA DONOGHUE

I once had brother that mother say we were pair of hands one fast one slow. I once had father he got lost in woods. I once had mother.

Huntman had wonderful beard. Let me and brother come too into the woods with gun. Brother help me make little house of branches.

But things changed after we held broom behind our hut and they jumped. Things went sour milk in churn all forgotten. Sky went far off and leaves went scrish scrish. Too cold for snow say mother. Put brother and me sleeping with chickens not annoy him.

One night hit her harder whap whap so her voice went big into rafters woke chickens say curse you.

Then on no luck for huntman. Means no meat for us. Brother say mother eat her words but I see only nuts and old bread. She put last drops holy water on huntman gun but still no luck. One night he come home snowed like pine. Next day lie in smelly furs all day bellyache. Bang fist on wall call angels to witness. Say How can we feed your children when we can't even feed ourselves?

Moonrise I holding chicken for warm hear him through wall. They talking small not like whap whap. She says It's their home. He say What's a home with a bare table?

Later after sounds like running I hear him say Pick one. You can't feed two birds with a single stone. The little one's no earthly use not right in the head.

After mother cry and gone quiet like sleeping I hold my head like apple shake it for see what sick. Sound alright but never can tell.

Morning mother red eyes but he let us come too into woods for rabbits brother and me. I dance like appledust. Trees come thicker round till no sky left. He tell brother go look at snare. He sit me behind tree for game. Make little fire give bread say no sound good girl.

I suck bread soft and wait for them come back. Cold. Sound like crows. Good girl but want home. Cry.

Lots hours later fire gone small. Hear feet think maybe lost father coming with acorn teeth and ivy where eyes were. Try run but fall on root.

Brother it was whistling. I call out. Don't cry little nut I found you I'll bring you home he say. Twice as old and ten times as clever. I put legs round waist and hold on.

Hut shine light but I feared. Stop at door. Seem like dark inside. Brother say Home again little hen. Lift latch mother cry but like happy. Huntman angered say Why did you get yourself lost you halfwit girl. He not remember game. No food on table but mother face wet salty.

Night they talking low again. Brother sleeping. I push chicken away put ear on wall. Huntman say Don't take on so, woman. Don't fight fate. You can have more when times are good again.

I think of having more food fire shoes till sleep.

Morning mother not get up. I want into furs with but he say woods again today. Walk lots hours. Where trees thickest he make small fire say Rest now like good children while I go deeper in to chop wood for a while. Brother want go with but huntman say Look after your sister or I'll beat the skin off you.

We wait. Lots hours later trees so thick no light at all outside fire. Sound like wolves. Fire tiny. Brother go for wood but I cry so he come back curl round me. Warm fart. Then no fire. He say Don't worry little loaf I'll bring you home as soon as it gets light.

Wake all covered snow cold but laugh. Throw ball brother. Home home home like song loud through snow. When brother wake face like old bread. Say he can't find way when all white. I say Follow me. Dance like snow home to mother.

Snow thicker feels like no feet no hands no noses. Brother follow me cry but try hide it.

When we see light I think morning. When we see cottage I think dreaming. Windows shine like sugar walls brown like ginger-bread.

Brother say Home but not so. Then brother say Come but I feared. I known wormy apples with shiny skin. I seen rotted teeth behind handsome beard. Brother go knock knock.

When door open I think mother but no. Young. Woman say What brought you here? No words from brother no words from me. Woman say Stop here with me tonight and no harm will touch you.

Bed so soft I think hot snow.

She wake me blowing on nose. I tell her walls gingerbread. She say And the door is toffee and the chimney is liquorice and the beds are chocolate. I not know words but laugh anyway. She make pancakes two each me her and brother. Her eyes red like crying but face smooth like girl.

We can stay if work. She know all that grow in woods. She know how talk rabbits into big cage in kitchen so never starving. Brother chop logs like grown man ask kiss get slap. She teach me roll dough for baking into shapes of woman tree star.

Only lonely nights. Wrap round brother like bread before oven. Very quiet say Home like it would get me there.

One night brother gone. I look out sugar crystal window but no steps in moon snow all swallowed up. Too feared to cry. Then woman scream like mother old nightmares say Get out of my bed. Brother fall on floor say Lonely.

Morning woman wake me stroking say Bonny red cheeks what will we do? Bake bread say I she laughing.

Days on days go by snow shrinks to nothing. I dance like white flowers pushing through cold head first. Brother has hair on chin instead of smile. Woman make him chop all trees died in winter till hands red like robins. I pick mouldy seeds from good.

One day we baking brother walk in call her name I never heard lift her skirt behind. Woman no scream this time. Put skinning knife to chin make drop of blood till he get in rabbit cage. He laughing as she chain it. I feared laughing. He shake cage but hold fast.

Night I cold so woman let me in with her. Make like she not hear brother shouting. I say He cold but she say Not for long.

I sleep warm between arms but wake up understanding she go to skin him like rabbit.

Slip into kitchen heart hanging like churn. Brother sleep till I find key in drawer open chain put hand over mouth.

He climb out stretching. Come on he whisper You're safe with me little nut.

Not safe anywhere.

He shake my head to wake it. Don't you understand? Now the snow is gone I can find our way home to mother.

No I crying quiet. Home not home if mother not mother.

But you can't stay here, she's mad, she's got a knife.

Take my chances I say.

He look for long while then nod head. I give him fresh bake loaf in shape of me. Tell him No come back with huntman gun. No came back ever.

I watch him run through trees. I lean head in door wait for woman to wake.

Sweeney's Lament in Mourne

SEAMUS HEANEY

It was snowing that night, and as fast as the snow fell, it was frozen. So he said:

—I have endured purgatories since the feathers grew on me. And still there is no respite. I realize, he said, that even if it were to mean my death, it would be better to trust my people than to endure these woes forever.

Then he recited the poem, proclaiming aloud his woes:

> Almighty God, I deserved this,
> my cut feet, my drained face,
> winnowed by a sheer wind
> and miserable in my mind.
>
> Last night I lay in Mourne
> plastered in wet; cold rain poured.
> To-night, in torment, in Glasgally
> I am crucified in the fork of a tree.
>
> I who endured unflinchingly
> through long nights and long days
> since the feathers penned my frame
> foresee nothing but the same.
>
> Hard weather has withered me,
> blizzards have buried me.
> As I wince here in cutting wind
> Glen Bolcain's heather haunts my mind.
>
> Unsettled, panicky, astray,
> I course over the whole country

from Liffey to Lower Bann,
from Bannside to the banks of Lagan;

then over Rathmore to Roscommon,
and fields that lie around Cruachan,
above Moylurg's level plain
and the brow of bushy Fews Mountain.

Or else I make a tough migration
to the Knockmealdown mountains;
or from Glasgally, a long glide
eastward to a Louth hillside.

All this is hard to thole, Lord!
Still without bed or board,
crouching to graze on cress,
drinking cold water from rivers.

Alarmed out of the autumn wood,
whipped by whins, flecked with blood,
running wild among wolf-packs,
shying away with the red stag.

Son of God, have mercy on us!
Never to hear a human voice!
To sleep naked every night
up there in the highest thickets,

to have lost my proper shape and looks,
a mad scuttler on mountain peaks,
a derelict doomed to loneliness:
Son of God, have mercy on us!

Admháil Shuaithinseach

Aon uair amháin riamh i mo shaol
a fuaireas oiread is an leide is lú ó bhéal
aon duine acu
go raibh saghas éigin cineghlanadh gafa tríd acu
is gur ó áit éigin eile ar fad, i bhfad i gcéin
a thángadar.

A sé déag nó mar sin a bhíos nuair a tharla sé seo.
Mé ag foghlaim bitheolaíochta
is teoirici ceimice.
Bhíos faoi dhraíocht ag fiseolaíocht agus sláinteachas
is mé lán suas
de théarmaí staidéir gnó is ríomhaireachta.

Thángas de shiúl cos lá treasna an Náth
mo threabhsar fillte suas go dtí mo chromáin
is smut de chruscar cladaigh á tharrac i mo dhiaidh agam.
Bhíos fiosrach faoi.
'Cén sórt bric í seo agam, a Thomáis?
Gadhar, ab ea?'

Do leag an seanduine uaidh a rámhainn ar an dtráigh
mar a raibh na luganna á mbaint aige.
Buí, dubhghlas is crón is ea do ghlioscadar
ag snámharnach de shíor sa chróca romhainn.
'Ní haon ghadhar é sin atá agat,' ar sé,
'ach cat. Cat ceannainn.'
Do stop sé, thug catshúil thapaidh deas is clé
is chuir cogar-i-leith chugham.

A Remarkable Revelation

NUALA NÍ DHOMHNAILL

Translated by Art Hughes

Only once in my whole life
did one of them
ever breathe the slightest word
about their people and their place
or that some had come from the land beyond the wave.

This was revealed to me as a sixteen-year-old
and avid student of biology
and chemical formulae,
who was also fascinated by physiology and hygiene,
and whose head was aswim
in the phraseology of accountancy and the data base.

I waded barefoot, trousers to the thigh,
across the river Nath, of an afternoon,
my curiousity aroused
—by the offal I was dragging behind me.
'What species of fish is this, Thomas?
Would it be a dog-fish?'

The old man stopped his digging for lug-worms
and laid to rest his spade on the strand,
but sun-yellow, murky green and tawny they squirmed
and wriggled all the while in his little jar.
'That's never a dog,' he began,
'it's a cat, a speckled cat-fish.'
He paused, gave a fleeting feline glance from side to side,
and beckoned me closer, to whisper:

'Níl aon ainmhí dá bhfuil ar an mintír,' ar sé,
'nach bhfuil a chomh-mhaith d'ainmhí
sa bhfarraige. An cat, an madra, an bhó, an mhuc,
tá siad go léir ann.
Go dtí an duine féin, agus tá sé sin ann leis.
Sé ainm atá air siúd ná an mhurúch.'

Ghluais scamail dorcha thar a shúile ar dhath na dtonn
a dhein tiompáin mhara dhóibh.
N'fheadar cad a shnámhaigh anall is anonn
sna duibheagáin doimhne sin
mar sara raibh am agam i gceart
é a bhodhradh le mo chuid cleatrála is le mo chaint
ar cheimic, fisic, is ar fhiosriúcháin muireolaíochta
do chas sé ar a shál is d'imigh uaim.

D'fhág sé ar snámh mé idir dhá uisce.

'Every species of animal that lives on the land
has its equal in the sea.
The cat, the dog, the cow, the pig,
they are all there.
Even humans are to be found
—the sea-folk.'

A dark sea-coloured cloud moves across his eyes,
by now two gaping oceans.
I shall never know what swam to and fro
in those abysmal depths
for, before I could avail of
unburdening onto him my babble and blether of
textbook science and marine biology
he turned on his heel and left.

He abandoned me there, floating between two waters.

Broken Homes

WILLIAM TREVOR

'I really think you're marvellous,' the man said.

He was small and plump, with a plump face that had a greyness about it where he shaved; his hair was grey also, falling into a fringe on his forehead. He was untidily dressed, a turtlenecked red jersey beneath a jacket that had a ballpoint pen and a pencil sticking out of the breast pocket. When he stood up his black corduroy trousers developed concertina creases. Nowadays you saw a lot of men like this, Mrs Malby said to herself.

'We're trying to help them,' he said, 'and of course we're trying to help you. The policy is to foster a deeper understanding.' He smiled, displaying small, evenly arranged teeth. 'Between the generations,' he added.

'Well, of course it's very kind,' Mrs Malby said.

He shook his head. He sipped the instant coffee she'd made for him and nibbled the edge of a pink wafer biscuit. As if driven by a compulsion, he dipped the biscuit into the coffee. He said:

'What age actually are you, Mrs Malby?'

'I'm eighty-seven.'

'You really are splendid for eighty-seven.'

He went on talking. He said he hoped he'd be as good himself at eighty-seven. He hoped he'd even be in the land of the living. 'Which I doubt,' he said with a laugh. 'Knowing me.'

Mrs Malby didn't know what he meant by that. She was sure she'd heard him quite correctly, but she could recall nothing he'd previously stated which indicated ill-health. She thought carefully while he continued to sip at his coffee and attend to the mush of biscuit. What he had said suggested that a knowledge of him would cause you to doubt that he'd live to old age. Had he already supplied further knowledge of himself which, due to her slight deafness, she had not heard? If he hadn't, why had he left everything hanging in the air like that? It was difficult to know how best to react, whether to smile or to display concern.

'So what I thought,' he said, 'was that we could send the kids on Tuesday. Say start the job Tuesday morning, eh, Mrs Malby?'

'It's extremely kind of you.'

'They're good kids.'

He stood up. He remarked on her two budgerigars and the geraniums on her window-sill. Her sitting-room was as warm as toast, he said; it was freezing outside.

'It's just that I wondered,' she said, having made up her mind to say it, 'if you could possibly have come to the wrong house?'

'Wrong? *Wrong?* You're Mrs Malby, aren't you?' He raised his voice. 'You're Mrs Malby, love?'

'Oh yes, it's just that my kitchen isn't really in need of decoration.'

He nodded. His head moved slowly and when it stopped his dark eyes stared at her from beneath his grey fringe. He said, quite softly, what she'd dreaded he might say: that she hadn't understood.

'I'm thinking of the community, Mrs Malby, I'm thinking of you here on your own above a greengrocer's shop with your two budgies. You can benefit my kids, Mrs Malby; they can benefit you. There's no charge of any kind whatsoever. Put it like this, Mrs Malby: it's an experiment in community relations.' He paused. He reminded her of a picture there'd been in a history book, a long time ago, History with Miss Deacon, a picture of a Roundhead. 'So you see, Mrs Malby,' he said, having said something else while he was reminding her of a Roundhead.

'It's just that my kitchen is really quite nice.'

'Let's have a little look, shall we?'

She led the way. He glanced at the kitchen's shell-pink walls, and at the white paintwork. It would cost her nearly a hundred pounds to have it done, he said; and then, to her horror, he began all over again, as if she hadn't heard a thing he'd been saying. He repeated that he was a teacher, from the school called the Tite Comprehensive. He appeared to assume that she wouldn't know the Tite Comprehensive, but she did: an ugly sprawl of glass-and-concrete buildings, children swinging along the pavements, shouting obscenities. The man repeated what he had said before about these children: that some of them came from broken homes. The ones he wished to send to her on Tuesday morning came from broken homes, which was no joke for them. He felt, he repeated, that we all had a special duty where such children were concerned.

Mrs Malby again agreed that broken homes were to be deplored. It was just, she explained, that she was thinking of the cost of decorating a kitchen which didn't need decorating. Paint and brushes were expensive, she pointed out.

'Freshen it over for you,' the man said, raising his voice. 'First thing Tuesday, Mrs Malby.'

He went away, and she realized that he hadn't told her his name. Thinking she might be wrong about that, she went over their encounter in her mind, going back to the moment when her doorbell had sounded. 'I'm from Tite Comprehensive,' was what he'd said. No name had been mentioned, of that she was positive.

In her elderliness Mrs Malby liked to be sure of such details. You had to work quite hard sometimes at eighty-seven, straining to hear, concentrating carefully in order to be sure of things. You had to make it clear you understood because people often imagined you didn't. Communication was what it was called nowadays, rather than conversation.

Mrs Malby was wearing a blue dress with a pattern of darker blue flowers on it. She was a woman who had been tall but had shrunk a little with age and had become slightly bent. Scant white hair crowned a face that was touched with elderly freckling. Large brown eyes, once her most striking feature, were quieter than they had been, tired behind spectacles now. Her husband, Ernest, the owner of the greengrocer's shop over which she lived, had died five years ago; her two sons, Derek and Roy, had been killed in the same month—June 1942—in the same desert retreat.

The greengrocer's shop was unpretentious, in an unpretentious street in Fulham called Catherine Street. The people who owned it now, Jewish people called King, kept an eye on Mrs Malby. They watched for her coming and going and if they missed her one day they'd ring her doorbell to see that she was all right. She had a niece in Ealing who looked in twice a year, and another niece in Islington, who was crippled with arthritis. Once a week Mrs Grove and Mrs Halbert came round with Meals on Wheels. A social worker, Miss Tingle, called; and the Reverend Bush called. Men came to read the meters.

In her elderliness, living where she'd lived since her marriage in 1920, Mrs Malby was happy. The tragedy in her life—the death of her sons—was no longer a nightmare, and the time that had passed since her husband's death had allowed her to come to terms with being on her own. All she wished for was to continue in these same circumstances until she died, and she did not fear death. She did not believe she would be reunited with her sons and her husband, not at least in a specific sense, but she could not believe, either, that she would entirely cease to exist the moment she ceased to breathe. Having thought about death, it seemed likely to Mrs Malby that after it came she'd dream, as in sleep. Heaven and hell were surely no more than flickers of such pleasant dreaming, or flickers of a nightmare from which there was no waking release. No loving omnipotent God, in Mrs Malby's view, doled out punishments and reward: human conscience, the last survivor, did that. The idea of a God, which had puzzled Mrs Malby for most of her life, made sense when she thought of it in terms like these, when she forgot about the mystic qualities claimed for a Church and for Jesus Christ. Yet fearful of offending the Reverend Bush, she kept such conclusions to herself when he came to see her.

All Mrs Malby dreaded now was becoming senile and being forced to enter the Sunset Home in Richmond, of which the Reverend Bush and Miss Tingle warmly spoke. The thought of a communal existence, surrounded by other elderly people, with sing-songs and card-games, was anathema to her. All her life she had hated anything that smacked of communal jolliness, refusing even to go on coach trips. She loved the house above the greengrocer's shop. She loved walking down the stairs and out on to the street, nodding at the Kings as she went by the shop, buying birdseed and eggs and fire-lighters, and fresh bread from Bob Skipps, a man of sixty-two whom she'd remembered being born.

The dread of having to leave Catherine Street ordered her life. With all her visitors she was careful, constantly on the lookout for signs in their eyes which might mean they were diagnosing her as senile. It was for this reason that she listened so intently to all that was said to her, that she concentrated, determined to let nothing slip by. It was for this reason that she smiled and endeavoured to appear agreeable and cooperative at all times. She was well aware that it wasn't going to be up to her to state that she was senile, or to argue that she wasn't, when the moment came.

After the teacher from Tite Comprehensive School had left, Mrs Malby continued to worry. The visit from this grey-haired man had bewildered her from the start. There was the oddity of his not giving his name, and then the way he'd placed a cigarette in his mouth and had taken it out again, putting it back in the packet. Had he imagined cigarette smoke would offend her? He could have asked, but in fact he hadn't even referred to the cigarette. Nor had he said where he'd heard about her: he hadn't mentioned the Reverend Bush, for instance, or Mrs Grove and Mrs Halbert, or Miss Tingle. He might have been a customer in the greengrocer's shop, but he hadn't given any indication that that was so. Added to which, and most of all, there was the consideration that her kitchen wasn't in the least in need of attention. She went to look at it again, beginning to wonder if there were things about it she couldn't see. She went over in her mind what the man had said about community relations. It was difficult to resist men like that, you had to go on repeating yourself and after a while you had to assess if you were sounding senile or not. There was also the consideration that the man was trying to do good, helping children from broken homes.

'Hi,' a boy with long blond hair said to her on the Tuesday morning. There were two other boys with him, one with a fuzz of dark curls all round his head, the other red-haired, a greased shock that hung to his shoulders. There was a girl as well, thin and beaky-faced, chewing something. Between them they carried tins of paint, brushes, cloths, a blue plastic bucket and a transistor radio. 'We come to do your kitchen out,' the blond boy said. 'You Mrs Wheeler then?'

'No, no. I'm Mrs Malby.'

'That's right, Billo,' the girl said. 'Malby.'

'I thought he says Wheeler.'

'Wheeler's the geyser in the paint shop,' the fuzzy-haired boy said.

'Typical Billo,' the girl said.

She let them in, saying it was very kind of them. She led them to the kitchen, remarking on the way that strictly speaking it wasn't in need of decoration, as they could see for themselves. She'd been thinking it over, she added: she wondered if they'd just like to wash the walls down, which was a task she found difficult to do herself?

They'd do whatever she wanted, they said, no problem. They put their paint tins on the table. The red-haired boy turned on the radio. 'Welcome back to Open House', a cheery voice said and then reminded its listeners that it was the voice of Pete Murray. It said that a record was about to be played for someone in Upminster.

'Would you like some coffee?' Mrs Malby suggested above the noise of the transistor.

'Great,' the blond boy said.

They all wore blue jeans with patches on them. The girl had a T-shirt with the words *I Lay Down With Jesus* on it. The others wore T-shirts of different colours, the blond boy's orange, the fuzzy one's light blue, the red-haired one's red. *Hot Jam-roll* a badge on the chest of the blond boy said; *Jaws* and *Bay City Rollers* other badges said.

Mrs Malby made them Nescafé while they listened to the music. They lit cigarettes, leaning about against the electric stove and against the edge of the table and against a wall. They didn't say anything because they were listening. 'That's a load of crap,' the red-haired boy pronounced eventually, and the others agreed. Even so they went on listening. 'Pete Murray's crappy,' the girl said.

Mrs Malby handed them the cups of coffee, drawing their attention to the sugar she'd put out for them on the table, and to the milk. She smiled at the girl. She said again that it was a job she couldn't manage any more, washing walls.

'Get that, Billo?' the fuzzy-haired boy said. 'Washing walls.'

'Who loves ya, baby?' Billo replied.

Mrs Malby closed the kitchen door on them, hoping they wouldn't take too long because the noise of the transistor was so loud. She listened to it for a quarter of an hour and then she decided to go out and do her shopping.

In Bob Skipps' she said that four children from the Tite Comprehensive had arrived in her house and were at present washing her kitchen walls. She said it again to the man in the fish shop and the man was surprised. It suddenly occurred to her that of course they couldn't have done any painting because she hadn't discussed colours with the teacher. She thought it odd that the teacher hadn't mentioned colours and wondered what colour the paint tins contained. It worried her a little that all that hadn't occurred to her before.

'Hi, Mrs Wheeler,' the boy called Billo said to her in her hall. He was standing there combing his hair, looking at himself in the mirror of the hall-stand. Music was coming from upstairs.

There were yellowish smears on the stair-carpet, which upset Mrs Malby very much. There were similar smears on the landing carpet. 'Oh, but please,' Mrs Malby cried, standing in the kitchen doorway. 'Oh, please, no!' she cried.

Yellow emulsion paint partially covered the shell-pink of one wall. Some had spilt from the tin on to the black-and-white vinyl of the floor and had been walked through. The boy with fuzzy hair was standing on a draining board applying the same paint to the ceiling. He was the only person in the kitchen.

He smiled at Mrs Malby, looking down at her. 'Hi, Mrs Wheeler,' he said.

'But I said only to wash them,' she cried.

She felt tired, saying that. The upset of finding the smears on the carpets and of seeing the hideous yellow plastered over the quiet shell-pink had already taken a toll. Her emotional outburst had caused her face and neck to become warm. She felt she'd like to lie down.

'Eh, Mrs Wheeler?' The boy smiled at her again, continuing to slap paint on to the ceiling. A lot of it dripped back on top of him, on to the draining board and on to cups and saucers and cutlery, and on to the floor. 'D'you fancy the colour, Mrs Wheeler?' he asked her.

All the time the transistor radio continued to blare, a voice inexpertly singing, a tuneless twanging. The boy referred to this

112

sound, pointing at the transistor with his paintbrush, saying it was great. Unsteadily she crossed the kitchen and turned the transistor off. 'Hey, sod it, missus,' the boy protested angrily.

'I said to wash the walls. I didn't even choose that colour.'

The boy, still annoyed because she turned off the radio, was gesturing crossly with the brush. There was paint in the fuzz of his hair and on his T-shirt and his face. Every time he moved the brush about paint flew off it. It speckled the windows, and the small dresser, and the electric stove and the taps and the sink.

'Where's the sound gone?' the boy called Billo demanded, coming into the kitchen and going straight to the transistor.

'I didn't want the kitchen painted,' Mrs Malby said again. 'I told you.'

The singing from the transistor recommenced, louder than before. On the draining board the fuzzy-haired boy began to sway, throwing his body and his head about.

'Please stop him painting,' Mrs Malby shouted as shrilly as she could.

'Here,' the boy called Billo said, bundling her out on to the landing and closing the kitchen door. 'Can't hear myself think in there.'

'I don't want it painted.'

'What's that, Mrs Wheeler?'

'My name isn't Wheeler. I don't want my kitchen painted. I told you.'

'Are we in the wrong house? Only we was told—'

'Will you please wash that paint off?'

'If we come to the wrong house—'

'You haven't come to the wrong house. Please tell that boy to wash off the paint he's put on.'

'Did a bloke from the Comp come in to see you, Mrs Wheeler? Fat bloke?'

'Yes, yes, he did.'

'Only he give instructions—'

'Please would you tell that boy?'

'Whatever you say, Mrs Wheeler.'

'And wipe up the paint where it's spilt on the floor. It's been trampled out, all over my carpets.'

'No problem, Mrs Wheeler.'

Not wishing to return to the kitchen herself, she ran the hot tap in the bathroom on to the sponge-cloth she kept for cleaning the bath. She found that if she rubbed hard enough at the paint on the stair-carpet and on the landing carpet it began to disappear. But the rubbing tired her. As she put away the sponge-cloth, Mrs Malby had a feeling of not quite knowing what was what. Everything that had happened in the last few hours felt like a dream; it also had the feeling of plays she had seen on television; the one thing it wasn't like was reality. As she paused in her bathroom, having placed the sponge-cloth on a ledge under the hand-basin, Mrs Malby saw herself standing there, as she often did in a dream: she saw her body hunched within the same blue dress she'd been wearing when the teacher called, and two touches of red in her pale face, and her white hair tidy on her head, and her fingers seeming fragile. In a dream anything could happen next: she might suddenly find herself forty years younger, Derek and Roy might be alive. She might be even younger; Dr Ramsey might be telling her she was pregnant. In a television play it would be different: the children who had come to her house might kill her. What she hoped for from reality was that order would be restored in her kitchen, that all the paint would be washed away from her walls as she had wiped it from her carpets, that the misunderstanding would be over. For an instant she saw herself in her kitchen, making tea for the children, saying it didn't matter. She even heard herself adding that in a life as long as hers you became used to everything.

She left the bathroom; the blare of the transistor still persisted. She didn't want to sit in her sitting-room, having to listen to it. She climbed the stairs to her bedroom, imagining the coolness there, and the quietness.

'Hey,' the girl protested when Mrs Malby opened her bedroom door.

'Sod off, you guys,' the boy with the red hair ordered.

They were in her bed. Their clothes were all over the floor. Her two budgerigars were flying about the room. Protruding from sheets and blankets she could see the boy's naked shoulders and the back of his head. The girl poked her face up from under him. She gazed at Mrs Malby. 'It's not them,' she whispered to the boy. 'It's the woman.'

'Hi there, missus.' The boy twisted his head round. From the kitchen, still loudly, came the noise of the transistor.

'Sorry,' the girl said.

'Why are they up here? Why have you let my birds out? You've no right to behave like this.'

'We needed sex,' the girl explained.

The budgerigars were perched on the looking-glass on the dressing-table, beadily surveying the scene.

'They're really great, them budgies,' the boy said.

Mrs Malby stepped through their garments. The budgerigars remained where they were. They fluttered when she seized them but they didn't offer any resistance. She returned with them to the door.

'You had no right,' she began to say to the two in her bed, but her voice had become weak. It quivered into a useless whisper, and once more she thought that what was happening couldn't be happening. She saw herself again, standing unhappily with the budgerigars.

In her sitting-room she wept. She returned the budgerigars to their cage and sat in an armchair by the window that looked out over Catherine Street. She sat in sunshine, feeling its warmth but not, as she might have done, delighting in it. She wept because she intensely disliked finding the boy and girl in her bed. Images from the bedroom remained vivid in her mind. On the floor the boy's boots were heavy and black, composed of leather that did not shine. The girl's shoes were green, with huge heels and soles. The girl's underclothes were purple, the boy's dirty. There'd been an unpleasant smell of sweat in her bedroom.

Mrs Malby waited, her head beginning to ache. She dried away her tears, wiping at her eyes and cheeks with a handkerchief. In Catherine Street people passed by on bicycles, girls from the polish factory returning home to lunch, men from the brickworks. People came out of the greengrocer's with leeks and cabbages in baskets, some carrying paper bags. Watching these

115

people in Catherine Street made her feel better, even though her headache was becoming worse. She felt more composed, and more in control of herself.

'We're sorry,' the girl said again, suddenly appearing, teetering on her clumsy shoes. 'We didn't think you'd come up to the bedroom.'

She tried to smile at the girl, but found it hard to do so. She nodded instead.

'The others put the birds in,' the girl said. 'Meant to be a joke, that was.'

She nodded again. She couldn't see how it could be a joke to take two budgerigars from their cage, but she didn't say that.

'We're getting on with the painting now,' the girl said, 'Sorry about that.'

She went away and Mrs Malby continued to watch the people in Catherine Street. The girl had made a mistake when she'd said they were getting on with the painting: what she'd meant was that they were getting on with washing it off. The girl had come straight downstairs to say she was sorry; she hadn't been told by the boys in the kitchen that the paint had been applied in error. When they'd gone, Mrs Malby said to herself, she'd open her bedroom window wide in order to get rid of the odour of sweat. She'd put clean sheets on her bed.

From the kitchen, above the noise of the transistor, came the clatter of raised voices. There was laughter and a crash, and then louder laughter. Singing began, attaching itself to the singing from the transistor.

She sat for twenty minutes and then she went and knocked on the kitchen door, not wishing to push the door open in case it knocked someone off a chair. There was no reply. She opened the door gingerly.

More yellow paint had been applied. The whole wall around the window was covered with it, and most of the wall behind the sink. Half of the ceiling had it on it; the woodwork that had been white was now a glossy dark blue. All four of the children were working with brushes. A tin of paint had been upset on the floor.

She wept again, standing there watching them, unable to prevent her tears. She felt them running warmly on her cheeks and then becoming cold. It was in this kitchen that she had cried first of all when the two telegrams had come in 1942, believing when the second one arrived that she would never cease to cry. It would have seemed ridiculous at the time, to cry just because her kitchen was all yellow.

They didn't see her standing there. They went on singing, slapping the paintbrushes back and forth. There'd been neat straight lines where the shell-pink met the white of the woodwork, but now the lines were any old how. The boy with the red hair was applying the dark-blue gloss.

Again the feeling that it wasn't happening possessed Mrs Malby. She'd had a dream a week ago, a particularly vivid dream in which the Prime Minister had stated on television that the Germans had been invited to invade England since England couldn't manage to look after herself anymore. That dream had been most troublesome because when she'd woken up in the morning she'd thought it was something she'd seen on television, that she'd actually been sitting in her sitting-room the night before listening to the Prime Minister saying that he and the Leader of the Opposition had decided the best for Britain was invasion. After thinking about it, she'd established that of course it hadn't been true; but even so she glanced at the headlines of the newspapers when she went out shopping.

'How d'you fancy it?' the boy called Billo called out to her, smiling across the kitchen at her, not noticing that she was upset. 'Neat, Mrs Wheeler?'

She didn't answer. She went downstairs and walked out of her hall door, into Catherine Street and into the greengrocer's that had been her husband's. It never closed in the middle of the day; it never had. She waited and Mr King appeared, wiping his mouth. 'Well then, Mrs Malby?' he said.

He was a big man with a well-kept black moustache and Jewish eyes. He didn't smile much because smiling wasn't his way, but he was in no way morose, rather the opposite.

'So what can I do for you?' he said.

She told him. He shook his head and repeatedly frowned as he listened. His expressive eyes widened. He called his wife.

While the three of them hurried along the pavement to Mrs Malby's open hall door it seemed to her that the Kings doubted her. She could feel them thinking that she must have got it all wrong, that she'd somehow imagined all this stuff about yellow paint and pop music on a radio, and her birds flying around her bedroom while two children were lying in her bed. She didn't blame them; she knew exactly how they felt. But when they entered her house the noise from the transistor could at once be heard.

The carpet of the landing was smeared again with the paint. Yellow footprints led to her sitting-room and out again, back to the kitchen.

'You bloody young hooligans,' Mr King shouted at them. He snapped the switch on the transistor. He told them to stop applying the paint immediately. 'What the hell d'you think you're up to?' he demanded furiously.

'We come to paint out the old ma's kitchen,' the boy called Billo explained, unruffled by Mr King's tone. 'We was carrying out instructions, mister.'

'So it was instructions to spill the blooming paint all over the floor? So it was instructions to cover the windows with it and every knife and fork in the place? So it was instructions to frighten the life out of a poor woman by messing about in her bedroom?'

'No one frightens her, mister.'

'You know what I mean, son.'

Mrs Malby returned with Mrs King and sat in the cubbyhole behind the shop, leaving Mr King to do his best. At three o'clock he arrived back, saying that the children had gone. He telephoned the school and after a delay was put in touch with the teacher who'd been to see Mrs Malby. He made his telephone call in the shop but Mrs Malby could hear him saying that what had happened was a disgrace. 'A woman of eighty-seven,' Mr King protested, 'thrown into a state of misery. There'll be something to pay on this, you know.'

There was some further discussion on the telephone, and then Mr King replaced the receiver. He put his head into the cubbyhole and announced that the teacher was coming round immediately to inspect the damage. 'What can I entice you to?' Mrs Malby heard him asking a customer, and a woman's voice replied that she needed tomatoes, a cauliflower, potatoes and Bramleys. She heard Mr King telling the woman what had happened, saying that it had wasted two hours of his time.

She drank the sweet milky tea which Mrs King had poured her. She tried not to think of the yellow paint and the dark-blue gloss. She tried not to remember the scene in the bedroom and the smell there'd been, and the new marks that had appeared on her carpets after she'd wiped off the original ones. She wanted to ask Mr King if these marks had been washed out before the paint had had a chance to dry, but she didn't like to ask this because Mr King had been so kind and it might seem like pressing him.

'Kids nowadays,' Mr King said. 'I just don't know.'

'Birched they should be,' Mr King said, coming into the cubbyhole and picking up a mug of the milky tea. 'I'd birch the bottoms off them.'

Someone arrived in the shop, Mr King hastened from the cubbyhole. 'What can I entice you to, Sir?' Mrs Malby heard him politely inquiring and the voice of the teacher who'd been to see her replied. He said who he was and Mr King wasn't polite any more. An experience like that, Mr King declared thunderously, could have killed an eighty-seven-year-old stone dead.

Mrs Malby stood up and Mrs King came promptly forward to place a hand under her elbow. They went into the shop like that. 'Three and a half p,' Mr King was saying to a woman who'd asked the price of oranges. 'The larger ones at four.'

Mr King gave the woman four of the smaller size and accepted her money. He called out to a youth who was passing by on a bicycle, about to start an afternoon paper round. He was a youth who occasionally assisted him on Saturday mornings: Mr King asked him now if he would mind the shop for ten minutes since an emergency had arisen. Just for once, Mr King argued, it wouldn't matter if the evening papers were a little late.

'Well, you can't say they haven't brightened the place up, Mrs

Malby,' the teacher said in her kitchen. He regarded her from beneath his grey fringe. He touched one of the walls with the tip of a finger. He nodded to himself, appearing to be satisfied.

The painting had been completed, the yellow and the dark-blue gloss. Where the colours had been spilt on the floor had been wiped away, but the black-and-white vinyl had become dull and grubby in the process. The paint had also been wiped from the windows and from other surfaces, leaving them smeared. The dresser had been wiped down and was smeary also. The cutlery and the taps and the cups and saucers had all been washed or wiped.

'Well, you wouldn't believe it!' Mrs King exclaimed. She turned to her husband. However had he managed it all? she asked him. 'You should have seen the place!' she said to the teacher.

'It's just the carpets,' Mr King said. He led the way from the kitchen to the sitting-room, pointing at the yellow on the landing carpet and on the sitting-room one. 'The blooming stuff dried,' he explained, 'before we could get to it. That's where compensation comes in.' He spoke sternly, addressing the teacher. 'I'd say she has a bob or two owing.'

Mrs King nudged Mrs Malby, drawing attention to the fact that Mr King was doing his best for her. The nudge suggested that all would be well because a sum of money would be paid, possibly even a larger sum than was merited. It suggested also that Mrs Malby in the end might find herself doing rather well.

'Compensation?' the teacher said, bending down and scratching at the paint on the sitting-room carpet. 'I'm afraid compensation's out of the question.'

'She's had her carpets ruined,' Mr King snapped quickly. 'This woman's been put about, you know.'

'She got her kitchen done free,' the teacher snapped back at him.

'They released her pets. They got up to tricks in a bed. You'd no damn right—'

'These kids come from broken homes, sir. I'll do my best with your carpets, Mrs Malby.'

'But what about my kitchen?' she whispered. She cleared her throat because her whispering could hardly be heard. 'My kitchen?' she whispered again.

'What about it, Mrs Malby?'

'I didn't want it painted.'

'Oh, don't be silly now.'

The teacher took his jacket off and threw it impatiently on to a chair. He left the sitting-room. Mrs Malby heard him running a tap in the kitchen.

'It was best to finish the painting, Mrs Malby,' Mr King said. 'Otherwise the kitchen would have driven you mad, half done like that. I stood over them till they finished it.'

'You can't take paint off, dear,' Mrs King said, 'once it's on. You've done wonders, Leo,' she said to her husband. 'Young devils.'

'We'd best be getting back,' Mr King said.

'It's quite nice, you know,' his wife added. 'Your kitchen's quite cheerful, dear.'

The Kings went away and the teacher rubbed at the yellow on the carpets with her washing-up brush. The landing carpet was marked anyway, he pointed out poking a finger at the stains left behind by the paint she'd removed herself with the sponge-cloth from the bathroom. She must be delighted with the kitchen, he said.

She knew she mustn't speak. She'd known she mustn't when the Kings had been there; she knew she mustn't now. She might have reminded the Kings that she'd chosen the original colours in the kitchen herself. She might have complained to the man as he rubbed at her carpets that the carpets would never be the same again. She watched him, not saying anything, not wishing to be regarded as a nuisance. The Kings would have considered her a nuisance too, agreeing to let children into her kitchen to paint it and then making a fuss. If she became a nuisance the teacher and the Kings would drift on to the same side, and the Reverend Bush would somehow be on that side also, and Miss Tingle, and even Mrs Grove and Mrs Halbert. They would agree among themselves that what had happened had to do with her elderliness, with her not understanding that children who brought paint into a kitchen were naturally going to use it.

'I defy anyone to notice that,' the teacher said, standing up, gesturing at the yellow blurs that remained on her carpets. He put his jacket on. He left the washing-up brush and the bowl of water he'd been using on the floor of her sitting-room. 'All's well that ends well,' he said. 'Thanks for your cooperation, Mrs Malby.'

She thought of her two sons, Derek and Roy, not knowing quite why she thought of them now. She descended the stairs with the teacher, who was cheerfully talking about community relations. You had to make allowances, he said, for kids like that; you had to try and understand; you couldn't just walk away.

Quite suddenly she wanted to tell him about Derek and Roy. In the desire to talk about them she imagined their bodies, as she used to in the past, soon after they'd been killed. They lay on desert sand, desert birds swooped down on them. Their four eyes were gone. She wanted to explain to the teacher that they'd been happy, a contented family in Catherine Street, until the war came and smashed everything to pieces. Nothing had been the same afterwards. It hadn't been easy to continue with nothing to continue for. Each room in the house had contained different memories of the two boys growing up. Cooking and cleaning had seemed pointless. The shop which would have been theirs would have to pass to someone else.

And yet time had soothed the awful double wound. The horror of the emptiness had been lived with, and if having the Kings in the shop now wasn't the same as having your sons there at least the Kings were kind. Thirty-four years after the destruction of your family you were happy in your elderliness because time had been merciful. She wanted to tell the teacher that also, she didn't know why, except that in some way it seemed relevant. But she didn't tell him because it would have been difficult to begin, because in the effort there'd be the danger of seeming senile. Instead she said good-bye, concentrating on that. She said she was sorry, saying it just to show she was aware that she hadn't made herself clear to the children. Conversation had broken down between the children and herself, she wanted him to know she knew it had.

He nodded vaguely, not listening to her. He was trying to make the world a better place, he said. 'For kids like that, Mrs Malby. Victims of broken homes.'

Fishing the Sloe-Black River

COLUM MCCANN

The women fished for their sons in the sloe-black river that ran through the small Westmeath town, while the fathers played football, without their sons, in a field half a mile away. Low shouts drifted like lazy swallows over the river, interrupting the silence of the women. They were casting with ferocious hope, twenty-six of them in unison, in a straight line along the muddy side of the low-slung river wall, whipping back the rods over their shoulders. They had pieces of fresh bread mashed onto hooks so that when they cast their lines the bread volleyed out over the river and hung for a moment, making curious contours in the air—cartwheels and tumbles and plunges. The bread landed with a soft splash on the water, and the ripples met each other gently.

The aurora borealis was beginning to finger the sky with light the colour of skin, wine bottles and the amber of the town's football jerseys. Drowsy clouds drifted, catching the colours from the north. A collie dog slept in the doorway of the only pub. The main street tumbled with litter.

The women along the wall stood yards apart, giving each other room so their lines wouldn't tangle. Mrs Conheeny wore a headscarf patterned with corgi dogs, the little animals yelping at the side of her ashy hair. She had tiny dollops of dough still stuck under her fingernails. There were splashes of mud on her wellingtons. She bent her back into the familiar work of reeling in the empty line. Each time she cast she curled her upper lip, scrunching up the crevices around her cheeks. She was wondering how Father Marsh, the old priest for whom she did housekeeping, was doing as goalkeeper. The joke around town was that he was only good for saving souls. As she spun a little line out from the reel she worried that her husband, at right half-back, might be feeling the ache in his knee from ligaments torn long ago.

Leaning up against the river wall, tall and bosom-burdened, she sighed and whisked her fishing rod through the air.

Beside her Mrs Harrington, the artist's wife, was a salmon leap of energy, thrashing the line back and forth as deftly as a fly fisherwoman, ripping crusts from her own loaves, impaling them on the big grey hook and spinning them out over the water's blackness, frantically tapping her feet up and down on the muddy bank. Mrs Harrington's husband had been shoved in at left full-forward in the hope that he might poke a stray shot away in a goalmouth frenzy. But by all accounts—or so Mr Conheeny said—the watercolour man wasn't worth a barman's fart on the football field. Then again, they all laughed, at least he was a warm body. He could fill a position against the other teams in the county, all of whom still managed to gallop, here and there, with young bones.

Mrs Conheeny scratched at her forehead. Not a bite, not a bit, not a brat around, she thought as she reeled in her line and watched a blue chocolate wrapper get caught in a gust of wind, then float down onto the water.

The collie left the door of the pub, ambling down along the main street, by the row of townhouses, nosing in the litter outside the newsagents. Heavy roars keened through the air as the evening stole shapes. Each time the women heard the whistle blow they raised their heads in the hope that the match was finished so they could unsnap the rods and bend towards home with their picnic baskets.

Mrs Conheeny watched Mrs Hynes across the river, her face plastered with make-up, tentatively clawing at a reel. Mrs King was there with her graphite rod. Mrs McDaid had come up with the idea of putting currants in her bread. Mrs O'Shaughnessy was whipping away with a long slender piece of bamboo—did she think she was fishing in the Mississippi? Mrs Bergen, her face scrunched in pain from the arthritis, was hoping her fingers might move a little better, like they used to on the antique accordion. Mrs Kelly was sipping from her little silver flask of the finest Jameson's. Mrs Hogan was casting with firefly-flicks of the wrist. Mrs Docherty was hauling in her line, as if gathering folds in her dress. And Mrs Hennessy was gently peeling the crust from a slice of Brennan's.

Further down along the pebbledashed wall Mrs McCarton

was gently humming a bit of a song. *Flow on lovely river, flow gently along, by your waters so clear sounds the lark's merry song.* Her husband captained the team, a barrel of a man who, when he was young, consistently scored a hat-trick. But the team hadn't won a game in two years, ever since the children had begun their drift.

They waited, the women, and they cast, all of them together.

When the long whistle finally cut through the air and the colours took on forms that flung themselves against the northern sky, the women slowly unsnapped their rods and placed the hooks in the lowest eyes. They looked at each other and nodded sadly. Another useless day fishing. Opening picnic baskets and lunch boxes, they put the bread away and waited for the line of Ford Cortinas and Vauxhalls and Opel Kadetts and Mr Hogan's blue tractor to trundle down and pick them up.

Their husbands arrived with their amber jerseys splattered with mud, their faces long in another defeat, cursing under taggles of pipes, their old bones creaking at the joints.

Mrs Conheeny readjusted her scarf and watched for her husband's car. She saw him lean over and ritually open the door even before he stopped. She ducked her head to get in, put the rod and basket in the back seat. She waved to the women who were still waiting, then took off her headscarf.

Any luck, love? he asked.

She shook her head: *I didn't even get a bite.*

She looked out to the sloe-black river as they drove off, then sighed. One day she would tell him how useless it all was, this fishing for sons, when the river looked not a bit like the Thames or the Darling or the Hudson or the Loire or even the Rhine itself, where their own three sons were working in a car factory. He slapped his hands on the steering wheel and said with a sad laugh: *Well fuck it anyway, we need some new blood in midfield,* although she knew that he too would go fishing that night, silently slipping out, down to the river, to cast in vain.

How to Catch a Chameleon

CLAIRR O'CONNOR

I did not catch a chameleon,
The elders did.
They beat the dried skin,
mixed it with the secret potion.
They made of our faces
a green mask.

Beauty, they called it
but I was watchful.
When we moved through the forest
or swam in the wide rivers,
our heads held above water
eyes turned to sky
I knew we were not blue of the river
or green of tree branches.
I felt only my neck twisted.

My cousin spoke in my ear,
'Stop your ugly words.
You insult the chameleon.
Your neck is gold-stretched
to beauty. Seven rings,
swim, smile.'

And what could I do?
The red flow had broken through.
The time had come, the time had come.
The elders knew all ceremonies.

To be picked first.
First bride from the river

bank. To be pulled from water
by him whose lips curl
darkly in kohl.
Also, his eyes, the whites
of teeth, white pillars
to be prized.

My head fell to water.
The chameleon fled
washed by water spirits.
I could not now be chosen.
I doubted.
My head drooped.
That is all.

When the wise one
shaved my head
and buried the troubled hairs
under the eucalyptus,
when my ancestors' bones beat shame
at the night feast,
when my father's eyes measured
my skeleton and my mother's back
spoke silence . . .
I knew their tent was full
without me.

The night came.
I followed the river,
I would not look back.

In the morning forest
drenched in light,
leaves dancing for the monkeys,
I ate nuts, whistled
like a boy-son.

'Windfall'

PAUL DURCAN

But, then, at the end of the day I could always say—
Well, now, I am going home.
I felt elected, steeped, sovereign to be able to say—
I am going home.
When I was at home I liked to stay at home;
At home I stayed at home for weeks;
At home I used sit in a winged chair by the window
Overlooking the river and the factory chimneys,
The electricity power station and the car assembly works,
The fleets of trawlers and the pilot tugs,
Dreaming that life is a dream which is real,
The river a reflection of itself in its own waters,
Goya sketching Goya among the smoky mirrors.
The industrial vista was my Mont Sainte-Victoire.
While my children sat on my knees watching TV
Their mother, my wife, reclined on the couch
Knitting a bright-coloured scarf, drinking a cup of black
    coffee,
Smoking a cigarette—one of her own roll-ups.
I closed my eyes and breathed in and breathed out.
It is ecstasy to breathe if you are at home in the world.
What a windfall! A home of our own!
Our neighbours' houses had names like 'Con Amore',
'Sans Souci', 'Pacelli', 'Montini', 'Homesville'.
But we called our home 'Windfall'.
'Windfall', 8 Parnell Hill, Cork.
In the gut of my head coursed the leaf of tranquillity
Which I dreamed was known only to Buddhist Monks
In lotus monasteries high up in the Hindu Kush.
Down here in the dark depths of Ireland,
Below sea level in the city of Cork,

In a city as intimate and homicidal as a Little Marseilles,
In a country where all the children of the nation
Are not cherished equally
And where the best go homeless, while the worst
Erect block-house palaces—self-regardingly ugly—
Having a home of your own can give to a family
A chance in a lifetime to transcend death.

At the high window, shipping from all over the world
Being borne up and down the busy, yet contemplative, river;
Skylines drifting in and out of skylines in the cloudy valley;
Firelight at dusk, and city lights;
Beyond them the control tower of the airport on the hill—
A lighthouse in the sky flashing green to white to green;
Our black-and-white cat snoozing in the corner of a chair;
Pastels and etchings on the four walls, and over the
    mantelpiece
'Van Gogh's Grave' and 'Lovers in Water';
A room wallpapered in books and family photograph albums
Chronicling the adventures and metamorphoses of family
    life:
In swaddling clothes in Mammy's arms on baptism day;
Being a baby of nine months and not remembering it;
Face-down in a pram, incarcerated in a high chair;
Everybody, including strangers, wearing shop-window
    smiles;
With Granny in Felixstowe, with Granny in Ballymaloe;
In a group photo in First Infants, on a bike at thirteen;
In the back garden in London, in the back garden in Cork;
Performing a headstand after First Holy Communion;
Getting a kiss from the Bishop on Confirmation Day;
Straw hats in the Bois de Boulogne, wearing wings at the
    seaside;
Mammy and Daddy holding hands on the Normandy
    Beaches;
Mammy and Daddy at the wedding of Jeremiah and
    Margot;

Mammy and Daddy queueing up for *Last Tango in Paris*;
Boating on the Shannon, climbing mountains in Kerry;
Building sandcastles in Killala, camping in Barley Cove;
Picnicking in Moone, hide-and-go-seek in Clonmacnoise;
Riding horses, cantering, jumping fences;
Pushing out toy yachts in the pond in the Tuileries;
The Irish College revisited in the Rue des Irlandais;
Sipping an *orange pressé* through a straw on the roof of the
    Beaubourg;
Dancing in Père Lachaise, weeping at Auvers.
Year in, year out, I pored over these albums accumulating,
My children looking over my shoulder, exhilarated as I was,
Their mother presiding at our ritual from a distance—
The far side of the hearthrug, diffidently, proudly.
Schoolbooks on the floor and pyjamas on the couch—
Whose turn is it tonight to put the children to bed?

Our children swam about our home
As if it was their private sea,
Their own unique, symbiotic fluid
Of which their parents also partook.
Such is home—a sea of your own—
In which you hang upside down from the ceiling
With equanimity, while postcards from Thailand on the
    mantelpiece
Are raising their eyebrow markings benignly:
Your hands dangling their prayers to the floorboards of
    your home,
Sifting the sands underneath the surfaces of conversations,
The marine insect life of the family psyche.
A home of your own—or a sea of your own—
In which climbing the walls is as natural
As making love on the stairs;
In which when the telephone rings
Husband and wife are metamorphosed into smiling
    accomplices,
Both declining to answer it;

Initiating, instead, a yet more subversive kiss—
A kiss they have perhaps never attempted before—
And might never have dreamed of attempting
Were it not for the telephone belling.
Through the bannisters or along the bannister rails
The pyjama-clad children solemnly watching
Their parents at play, jumping up and down in support,
Race back to bed, gesticulating wordlessly:
The most subversive unit in society is the human family.

We're almost home, pet, almost home . . .
Our home is at . . .
I'll be home . . .
I have to go home now . . .
I want to go home now . . .
Are you feeling homesick?
Are you anxious to get home? . . .
I can't wait to get home . . .
Let's stay at home tonight and . . .
What time will you be coming home at? . . .
If I'm not home by six at the latest, I'll phone . . .
We're nearly home, don't worry, we're nearly home . . .

But then with good reason
I was put out of my home:
By a keen wind felled.
I find myself now without a home
Having to live homeless in the alien, foreign city of
Dublin.
It is an eerie enough feeling to be homesick
Yet knowing you will be going home next week;
It is an eerie feeling beyond all ornithological analysis
To be homesick knowing that there is no home to go to:
Day by day, creeping, crawling,
Moonlighting, escaping,
Bed-and-breakfast to bed-and-breakfast;
Hostels, centres, one-night hotels.

Homeless in Dublin,
Blown about the suburban streets at evening,
Peering in the windows of other people's homes,
Wondering what it must feel like
To be sitting around a fire—
Apache or Cherokee or Bourgeoisie—
Beholding the firelit faces of your family,
Beholding their starry or their TV gaze:
Windfall to Windfall—can you hear me?
Windfall to Windfall . . .
We're almost home, pet, don't worry anymore, we're
    almost home.

Roma

EUGENE MCCABE

Maria came out of the kitchen with a fish supper.

'It's here, Mickey, on the counter.'

Wiping the mock terrazzo he thanked her from his knees, no press stud in his cap, the peak almost level with his foggy glasses. He seemed blind. She sat at a formica-topped table near the juke-box, opened a magazine and watched him get up. Not his fault the way he looked, yellow teeth in red gums, the face white like a monk's. That was why kids chucked things as he pulled his barrow through streets, women giggling in doorways when their men tonguefarted or used the Holy Name. A bit of crack, they thought, to see him drop the handcart and bless himself. Of course he was odd, out praying like that from house to house, and when he wasn't carting brock or clearing dumps he sat in the loft he shared with Joe the Bush down their yard. Joe was part-time beggar, full-time drunk. One day she asked Joe what Mickey did in the loft.

'Never done cuttin' slips from wee Holy Books and stickin' them in copy books with Holy pictures . . . the kind of thing an auld nun puts in her time at.' Holy Mickey, mad Mickey, Mickey the mutter, Mickey the brock, Mickey Longford, he had nicknames enough to do ten townlands. She had never really bothered much with him till yesterday when Connolly took him away to load pigs. He had left the garden in a hurry, his jacket bunched in the fork of a tree. Hanging clothes on the line she could see a wad of stuff in the breast pocket. There was no one about. Under an apple tree she went through the wad, bits of paper, clippings, mostly handprinted, with different coloured biros.

She read:

c/o Digacimo

Café Roma

The Diamond

The World is Dying

The Town is Dying.

A Cure for the World

Shut the Pubs
Shut the Dance Halls
Shut the Picture Houses
Put cars off the roads
More Penance
Live Modest
Think on death day and night,
Bad thoughts make bad Talk
Makes man do bad things
After that the head goes
Burn Dirty Books, Papers and Pictures
Pray for my father in the mental, keep him
from Hell
Pray for my Mother in her grave at Knockatallon
Pray for Annie and Josie who have forgot me
Pray for Joe the Bush who sins every night
Pray for people who shout at me and childer who
mock me
Pray for Mr and Mrs Digacimo, and M
Above all things keep M pure

Sellotaped to a piece of cardboard was a picture of the Virgin
waistdeep in cotton wool. Printed carefully underneath:
MARIA
May God scatter over her path the Flower of His
Divine Benediction

She began to feel she had encroached and fumbled the wad.
Medals, scapulars, notes and letters fell on the grass. As she gathered them one caught her eye. It began with her name:

Maria I must tell you things The truth In the yard at night I
often stand under your room I would like to be the light in your
room I could see you then and give light for your homework I

would stay awake all night watching you breathe that's all Odd times too I would like to be slippers you wear about the house and cafe or the sheets in your bed or your comb in the streets I am crying to myself because of you my life is terrible and there is nothing I can do the squeal of pigs I hate and the smell of them makes me sick every day I see little pigs sucking out of big ones and the big ones breed like rats acres of them out at clonfad a town of pigs beside the town when they are fat for the factory I help load them on the lorries the smell is awful on a hot day blood and squeeling in the factory yard do they know I often wonder most people eat sausages even you I don't it makes me sick everything does in this world except you I can't explain it nothing is new to me before I sleep you are my gate to heaven when I wake you are my morning star and the truth is the heart is broke inside me because of how I feel and I can never tell you or give you this letter I write this because it is the truth maybe I'll give it to you sometime but I don't think so

Guilty, she had gathered the stuff and put it back in the wad. All that evening she felt disturbed. It broke her sleep and this morning she woke early. All day it had been with her and now near the juke-box she waited, watching him begin to eat.

He could feel her eyes. Sometimes of a Saturday when the café was closed she came in like this and sat looking through the magazine, an overall over her school uniform. Odd times she'd play a record on the machine or move about herself, making noises with her fingers. Other times she'd join her mother and father in the kitchen. They sat there most Saturday nights when the place was shut, reading out of foreign papers, hard workers who kept to themselves. No friends; much like myself.

'How old are you, Mickey?'

She was looking at him very straight, eyes in her head like no other girl or woman body he ever knew.

'Is that a cheeky thing to ask?'

'I'm six and thirty.'

She went back to her magazine. He looked up at the panel

above the steel chipper, painted in shopgloss by Murray the decorator; Pope John smiling before Saint Peter's, hand upraised in blessing; beside him President Kennedy smiling before the White House, hands in jacket pocket addressing the world through a megaphone. He put a chip in his mouth.

'Why are you so grey?'

'The breed of me, nature I suppose.'

'Are you long left home?'

'I quit home when my mother died. I was glad to quit.'

'But you're from this country?'

'I'm a Longford man, here this brave while. I mind when you were born, people sayin' "them Italians have a daughter".'

'You were here then, Mickey?'

'About the town.'

'Working?'

'When I could.'

'At what?'

'Anything.'

'And your people; what did they do?'

'The auld fellow was a blacksmith when he was sober . . . he drank wild.'

'Is he dead too?'

'In the Mental, below in Mullingar: God blacked his mind, he broke my mother's heart, let the roof fall in, and the whole place go to rack. I couldn't stop him. I've two sisters married in England.'

'You see them?'

'No.'

'Do they write?'

'No.'

'Don't you?'

'Not this brave while. They have fambleys of their own, it's natural.'

He couldn't keep looking into her eyes so he looked away. She put money in the machines and played a record. It made a noise like pigs being castrated to the sound of drums; when it stopped she asked:

'Do you ever see him, your father?'

'He didn't know me last time, and let a shout: "I have no son, I'm the Holy Ghost, I have no son." Then he started in to laugh and giggle and wink and said all classes of bad things. It's on account of his rotten life. God's punishment for the dark things he had done when he was drunk.'

'What things? Was he bad?'

'I'd call him bad.'

'What did he do?'

'He was bad.'

'Papa says you shouldn't be sleeping down the yard with Joe or carting brock about the streets. He says it's a great pity of you, that you're a strange person.'

'Every man has some oddness.'

She had never talked close before. He felt clumsy. He moved his knife about the table.

'Am I annoying you?'

'No.'

'If I didn't ask you'd say nothing. Sometimes you go a month without saying a word. Why?'

'No call to . . . anyway . . .'

'Yes?'

'You're too young.'

'For what?'

'To know.'

'What?'

'Maria! Maria!' Mrs Digacimo's voice called high in the house.

'Si, Mama?'

The voice said something in their speech. As she got up to leave she said:

'You'll have to tell me what I don't know. I'll be back.'

He watched her walk up the terrazzo floor under the fluorescent lighting past Pope John and President Kennedy, past the glossy murals of old buildings and bridges falling down across fields, past the tower going sideways and streets full of boats, and through the beaded string opening that led to the house.

What was it he couldn't tell her? There were things a grown

man couldn't tell a growing girl, specially her. He couldn't say the loft he shared with Joe the Bush faced a pub entry and how night about he could hear the pissing and puking, the gropes and groans of men and women, or of how he saw his auld fellow drunk once in a shed, or remark on how Joe the Bush abused himself night after night. Even to-night when he came in to wash the floor Cissy Caffery and young Mulligan sat on facing each other. Mulligan had his hand up Cissy's skirt and she not fifteen and the two of them talking and laughing with no trace of shame. Course they were young. You had to allow for that. Maybe God would look gentle on hot blood, but there were other things so bad you couldn't scour them from your mind. The world was sick and the more he saw the worse it got. Sometimes it seemed God was deaf or blind or gone asleep. Sometimes it seemed there was no cure.

The lights in the café went out and the hood of the chipper caught the street lighting, and made the two Johns a pair of grinning ghosts. He heard someone again on the staircase.

Maria came into the café and made her way through the dark tables to where she had left her magazine. Still there; alone. The street lights made him seem unreal, like the morning early she looked down from her window to the yard. He was standing against the gable of the coach house, grey face and head, arms outstretched. She had put on her dressing-gown and watched. Holy Mickey, Mickey the mutter, Mickey Longford. What she had read in the wallet was so strange, somehow private, she meant to keep to herself, but to-day when Ursula Brogan began boasting again about the Old Ward man who always stopped her and held her hand she found herself talking about Mickey. Ursula listened and said:

'Ah God, that's awful. I'd straighten him out, Maria, honest to God I would.'

'It's nice someway.'

'The Blessed Virgin . . . It's pukey!'

'But I am a virgin.'

'Not the Blessed Virgin. It's not right. I'd tell him if I were you.'

'Tell him what?'

He moved in the chair as she approached. She could just make him out.

'Did we leave you in the dark again, Mickey?'

'No odds. I'm for bed.'

She moved to see him better and said:

'What am I too young to know?'

Mickey heard her voice but didn't know what she had asked. It was darkness all round but where she stood it seemed light. For a moment he thought he'd like to go down on his knees and kiss her hands and feet.

'Pardon, Miss.'

'What am I too young to know?'

'The world is bad, Miss.'

'Sure I know that.'

'And this town is rotten like the bad end of a city.'

'Ah come off it, Mickey, how do you know?'

'I hear it and see it.'

'Where?'

'Down the yard, round the town, out the country, everywhere. No one thinks of God or dying or what comes after.'

She looked out towards the street. She was holding the magazine against her breast, exactly as the Virgin held the child in a picture he had, but much younger, more beautiful. He wanted to say he'd die to keep her the way she was, clear of the Mulligans and Joe the Bush, the pubs, the drunks, the women in the doorways, the pigs and the dance-halls, the brock, all the ugliness of life. She was like a sloping field one spring day he remembered long ago in Longford, high high hedges that hid houses, roads, lanes. You could see nothing but sky. Just grass, thorn blossom and the sky. It was so beautiful he felt that it would blind him. He wanted to sleep and never wake. That was what she was like looking out in the street. He had the same feeling now that he got in the field, but how did you say a thing like that? Then he heard himself say:

'You're like a field.'

'A field?'

Did she give a little giggle? He wasn't sure.

'At home near Knockatallon. It had high hedges.'

He knew he couldn't say the thing he thought.

'A field in May . . . thorn ditches . . . there was a power of blossom.'

For quite a time neither said anything. Then Maria said:

'I'm not like that; I know what you mean but I'm not like that. When you said a field I nearly laughed because I was in a field last week with Ursula Brogan behind the football pitch. We followed Cissy Caffery there and two boys from the secondary. She's a wagon. She did it with them one after the other, and we watched.'

The street lights went out. The silence was odd. She felt she must go on talking:

'I wouldn't do that but if I loved a fellow I'd lie with him and make him happy. That's the truth about me. Are you there, Mickey?'

'Yes.'

'You heard what I said?'

'Why did you say it?'

'It's true.'

'You shouldn't.'

'Have watched or told you?'

He didn't answer. His chair scraped and she saw him move towards the kitchen.

'Mickey!'

He went through the kitchen out the back door down the yard. She could feel the heat in her face and an odd beat in her heart. It had seemed right to tell him, but as she spoke it sounded blunt, ugly and final as though she were deliberately destroying something; false too because she'd been disgusted and didn't say so. 'But I didn't mean anything' she thought. What made her say it when she knew what he'd written and how he thought about her, it was like mocking a cripple or putting poison in a baby's bottle.

She went down the yard and looked up at the loft; no light. Even if she did see him how could she unsay what she had said. She felt now she was worse than Cissy Caffery, that she had done something very stupid and very wrong and there was no way she could undo it.

'I'm sorry, Mickey. Honestly I'm sorry.'

He sat in the loft on the iron frame bed. Twice Joe the Bush said something to him. Mickey heard words but couldn't give them meaning.

'Are you deaf, man?'

'What?'

'Why don't ya spake?'

'What?'

'Arra God!'

Mickey lay back on the bed dressed and looked through the skylight at the stars. Joe the Bush began to shift about, abusing himself as he did most nights. The springs skreeked and the broken castor scraped on the wormy boards. Mickey listened.

'God sees you, Joe.'

'For Christ's sake shut up, you eejit. They'll lock you up like your father.'

Then Joe was snoring and Mickey was counting hours from the Church. Again and again he scoured his mind with prayer, but he could see her eyes seeing what she said she'd seen, her mouth telling nakedness and sin and for an instant he saw her lying with Joe the Bush and he woke startled and sweating. Why had she said such things? Would she earn Hell too with filthy hags, a hag herself, her mouth black and screaming, damned? What was happening to the world? Men, women and children walking to damnation. The stars were mostly gone when he found himself saying: 'House of Gold, Ark of the Covenant, Gate of Heaven, Morning Star, Morning Star, Morning Star.' Winter and there were stars over the frosted field and he was kneeling on hard ground waiting for the Mother of God, Christ born again in this field at Knockatallon. He'd be there and the world saved. An ass carrying a small cloaked figure came through the frozen gap. A hatted man behind kept prodding. He could see it all very clearly, even the mincing trot of the ass, its tail wagging . . . It was Saint Joseph and the Virgin Mary. The ass came up the field to where he was kneeling. Mary dismounted and began opening a pack. He could tell she was very young, a girl. Saint Joseph made an arch of blackened ash rods and pulled a tat of bags across it. He lit a fire at the opening of the tent and sat. The Virgin took something out of the pack and crept over beside him. He saw then it was Maria and Joe the Bush and she had a bottle of whiskey and they were swigging it now and laughing and after a while Joe whispered something. She smiled, and put her head in his lap. Mickey closed his eyes. There was a terrible noise of animals and humans squealing, shrieking together like the pigs at Clonfad and something in his head was saying: Help of the Weak, Refuge of Sinners, Comforter of the Afflicted, but the noise got louder and above it clearly he could see her beautiful head in Joe's lap and Joe was holding it when suddenly Joe was shouting: 'Christ!' and then 'Oh Christ! Christ, Christ, Christ' and pushed her from him. She spat, picked up the bottle of whiskey and drank till it was empty. She looked round and at him with lost eyes, a sag in her mouth, her face blotched, her hair a dirty frizz like old Maggie Greggan of the Gullet. There was a smell from them like the smell in Connolly's boar-sty, so strong he could hardly breathe. He tried to get up. He couldn't. The smell got worse and began to smell like corruption and death and he couldn't breathe now at all because the smell was so bad and he was retching and then he was sitting up in bed choking and crying.

The stars were gone. In the corner of the loft Joe the Bush was asleep, his mouth open like a black hole in a grey stubble. It made him feel sick to look at Joe. He thought for a while, got up and strapped what he had into a blanket, emptied a box of clippings into a cardboard bin and went down the ladder. Grey light in the flagged yard. The slates of a disused bakery showed rain; church, houses, streets and fields seemed huddled, condemned. He washed at a tap in the yard. The water splashed on pocked cement and ran away down a blind gully that went under the dripping apple trees. He carried the cardboard box to a bare patch beside a plum tree and set fire to it. As it burned he dropped everything from the wad keeping only his mother's memorial card. He watched the flames twist and warp and said aloud, 'I'd like to be dead and buried, yes that's a fact.' When the papers were ash he went back to the yard and looked up at the stucco house and read the words on the wall:

CAFÉ ROMA

SNACKS, FISH SUPPERS, ACCOMMODATION.

A black plastic sewage pipe came down the middle of the house, past her open window with its blue curtains.

'I'll not think,' he said, 'I'll go.'

Then he turned to climb the pipe. It was wet and slippery. He went down the stone staircase to the basement and got in the scullery window. Up then to the street hall with the arched doorway, big photographs, the table and two chairs. Up again the rubbernosed staircase to the upper landing with its one high window looking north. There was brown lino on the floor, a big green plant in a brass pot. Five doors. That was hers, open. He could see the blue curtains, her school uniform on a chair. He went in. She was deep asleep, breathing easy, beautiful as any picture he ever saw:

'Impure.'

Her eyes opened:

'Impure,' he shouted, 'dirty.'

She got up on her elbows. He could hear himself but wasn't sure what he was saying. Then there was trembling and crying and muttering. Maria was startled. She felt no fear just pity, and shame.

'Mickey, I'm sorry. Please. Don't. You're shouting, you'll wake them. Please go, please.'

'Impure, dirty, dirty, dirty.'

Then Mr Digacimo was standing in the room in pyjamas, the hair he combed carefully across his pate hanging down over one ear. Mickey was muttering:

'God Almighty's Mother, a bitch fit for any mongrel, dirty, impure.'

Mr Digacimo took his arm.

Maria said:

'Please Papa, he means nothing, he's upset.'

Mickey pulled away and left the room. He saw Mr Digacimo on the landing in an overcoat. He heard her say something that sounded like Police. He went out the back door to the yard, put the strapped blanket on the handcart and pushed it up the entry of the street.

'I'll not think, I'll go.'

He went out the west road heading for Leitrim. He heard a man say once there was nothing left in Leitrim now but bare mountains, empty houses and the bones of sheep. The hedges gave way to a straggle of whins. He looked back and down. The town was gone in a smore of rain. She too would die in his mind and be forgot, like when a body died. Later there were cars, trucks and vans; children on a school bus looked out pointing and laughing. He went up a branch road. He would find his way through side roads and lanes. There was no going back. Tired he sat on a ditch and looked at the country, the sun lost in clouds, thousands of crows flying somewhere, over dark lakes, November again, a thin wind, and the fields sodden.

An old man came up the road driving two bony cows. He had fag-coloured stubble and smoky eyes, a withered face like his father's:

'Where are you going with the handcart, son?'

'Leitrim.'

'Where to?'

'I don't know.'

The old man stared. Mickey got up and said, 'I must go.' The old man said nothing, then spat and called:

'Good luck to you, son, and Leitrim.'

Later he would pray when he could think easy. As long as you had God and his Blessed Mother it was no odds where you were going, or when you got there. He must keep to that and burn all else from his mind: that was truth. Then he said aloud:

'My heart is broken, that's the truth; my love is dead, that's a fact.'

Patera

DESMOND HOGAN

'You'll never fit in here,' an Irish woman whom I very vaguely knew told me when I came to live in London permanently. It was on a street in West London, still war-time colours—teal-blues, Santa Claus reds—lamp-posts like liquorice twisters, a pastel billboard for rock fish, scampi, skate, cod roe, saveloy, spam fritters, outside Gunn's fish and chip shop, fly-blown glass. 'The West Indians, the Indians fit in here. But the Irish, never.' A very fat young man in a black, collared T-shirt, a scarlet line in the collar, stood on the street, an earring in each ear.

Afterwards, about a year later, I had tea in that woman's small and sparse flat. A photograph on the wall of a visit to New York— a girl with a sixties bouffant in a blue-grey dress with white constellations on it against cornflower blue skyscrapers. A photograph of girls in emergent strawberry chequered dresses outside a country cottage. A wedding photograph, a woman in a turban hat with wings at the back standing very straight beside the girl with the sixties bouffant who looked more ill at ease than she'd been in New York. White crockery with borders of alternate squares of blue and pink roses in a cabinet.

A black woman, in a hip-length jacket walks, head in the air, with a bunch of salmon-coloured carnations by the station at Champion Park.

A boy with shorn hair holds the hand of a little girl in a long tartan dress with an Eton collar and button-up patent boots.

On the railway platform a young British Rail worker stands, military shoulders, cropped hair, in mauve-carmine shoes with blond bristles on them, dunes in his face.

A boy darts among the congregation of homeless near Victoria Station, hands behind his back, red military cap on his head.

'Why are you wearing the beret? Are you in the Foreign Legion?'

'Do you remember Bridget the Midget?' two tramps are in conversation on the ground near me.

A boy who said he was doubly incontinent and that he'd been an alcoholic since he was twenty asks about the trains back to Nottingham.

'Where are you going to sleep tonight?' the boy in the military beret shouts at a woman whose head is annealed by many scarves.

A former tramp called Rose, in a pink taffeta dress, on crutches, has come to visit her former companions. 'I live in Kings Cross now. Dreadful place. Six-year-olds beat up old women.'

In an arcade a Liverpool boy sings a song he'd written himself: 'I want to go home.'

On the journey to Ostend, in a part of the ship deserted but for the two of us, an old Jewish man in a hat and in a prayer shawl, tallow and black striped, leans over a table, quietly droning prayers for those at sea.

In Antwerp Central Station there is a fanfare of yellow embossments on the caféteria wall. The chandeliers are gold cylinders. Little nuns in oyster grey slouch by and the men's lavatory is filled with mimosa and gypsophila and women in flowered dresses. At the caféteria counter someone in a beige jersey carded with London smells leans towards me as if to say something.

The trimming of the city across the square from the station— lime trees, plane trees, advertisements for McDonald's.

A tramp walks his bicycle with all his belongings on it by the station.

'Most people think we're just dossers. They don't know the background,' a tramp had told me outside Victoria Station before I got the train.

A man in a sailor's cap, a black sleeveless jersey, blows a gold horn which had been hanging around his neck, by the river, to announce the departure of a boat. A man with a bald head like unopened hawthorn blossom is staring at the river.

In a Jewish café near the station I have a coffee and warm almond boluses. On the wall is a black and white photograph of an old Jewish lady giving chrysanthemums to Princess Juliana, September 9, 1938, in the Jewish Invalid Hospital.

The streets in Amsterdam are like cobwebs on plantation oaks in the Southern States—the windows and transoms of bars and cafés crowded with things, the packed flotsam of one window connecting with that of another—dolls in flamingo silks, stains on their faces and the same stains running over pigs clasping their breasts; cups in the shape of buxom monks; cowled monks with their hands enveloped in their gowns; the head of Winston Churchill, cheeks very rouged, ruff at his neck; cherubs throwing their legs in the air like can-can dancers; a teddybear in a cage with monkeys painted on tympanums beneath him; a Droste's cocoa tin—burnt orange—with a girl in Dutch costume carrying pails on it; a small placard—*Je ne fume que le Nils*—with a girl in lavender robes and raffia sandals smoking a cigar by the Nile; a pig chanteuse with long gloves, blonde sideswept hair; a bear doctor with a stethoscope; Santa Claus with a hyacinthine beard, little purple bells and acorns in it; two huge swans, one on either side, hem in a table with Turkish weaving on it—purple with yellow, orange and olive flowers; a pyramid of tins of Fanta, Coke in the window of a Turkish café, the ceiling scuffed with little black marks; a display of pear flans, forest berry bavarois, orange cakes with a litter of little orange fruit on them, mounds of white smoothed icing; piles of Disque Bleu cigarettes; heaps of many coloured buttons, some in transparent tubes.

Stone beavers snuggle into seventeenth-century dates on the wall; there's a Moor in dog-rose garb. In the windows are camellias, liatris, purple statice; tin pitchers of daisies outside houses.

Years ago I knew a girl from Galway who came here and had a flat near the Casa Rosso nightclub, a shower of fuschine lights on the canal outside at night. I met her in Amsterdam once, in a café where a Chinese man was sitting under photographs of Buddhist monasteries, on a day of autumn sunshine. I was with a girl who had lemon yellow hair. The girl from Galway was wearing a blouse with yellow ducks on it. She died in Amsterdam some months after that, of a heroin overdose.

A girl in a Leghorn hat with a red cloth rose in it and in a dress of double squares of pale blue on white, red roses at the edges of the squares, cycles by and looks directly into my eyes, first time in months it seems someone looks directly into my eyes.

A woman in a dress of pale yellow with squares of pale blue linen, dark blue corners to the squares, stands outside a pigeon shop.

A little girl and boy walk by in white, both in scarlet sneakers, a Pekinese with a scarlet ribbon on its head looks down on them from a window.

In another square an old Ashkenazi Jewish man with cork-screw curls smokes a pipe with a fist carved at the end of it. A barge comes through a narrow canal.

The women in flowered dresses, one of the dresses with a white collar, sit on a wall in a little cul de sac, a Turkish woman in white behind them, a ceramic rooster in a transom.

In the Saint Francis Xavier Church on Singel a woman and little boy light a candle in front of a statue of a gold Virgin with rubric undersleeves and a child with a gold bracelet on his wrist and a gold apple in his hand.

Moving always reminds me of one-storey houses of London brick orange between the South Circular Road and the Grand Canal, with mustard or green doors and flaxen stains on the lace curtains and crockery with Greek key patterns in the windows and a sense of lives within with gashes in them.

My relationship with England once was the harebell-blue of the sea between Calais and Folkestone in November, coming back from days of the Riviera dei Fiori, having lost my passport, being interrogated by police who'd inspect a card from a tiny hotel on the Passeggiata di Via Roma, Alassio or a postcard of an ivory Virgin.

When I first arrived in London in 1970, after getting a room in Kilburn, the first outing I made was to Hampstead Heath. It was July, late afternoon, and the houses on the margin of the Heath were lighted up, wine doors, diamond shapes and flowers in the lace curtains, lozenge shapes in the transoms, Japanese red maple trees in cobbled front yards, white rose bushes, great terracotta pots placed in bohemian nonchalance.

There'd been an Italian man in a Zouave cap hanging like a plum to one side with a dancing bear in a fair on the Heath.

In the following few weeks I saw sunflowers, lobelias, chrysanthemums, geraniums, candytuft, autumn narcissi, saffron, lavender, poppies, jasmine come to those gardens. I sat on benches with many arms, fretwork of Nile green and turquoise, with single nettles or fool's parsley coming through them as though waiting for a partner.

The names on the War Memorial at the top of the Heath, against the autumn sunsets, were Gildersleeves, Cloutman, Wolfred, Budd, Plaistowe, Selbie, Dawbarn, Younge, Sandalay, Samuels, Schleichert, Howlett.

In the town I came from, which I'd left a year before to go to university in Dublin, there'd been a little Royal British Legion hut, under chestnut trees, when I was a child, with war memorials inside to those killed in Ypres and Givenchy, names like Hanaffy, Munnelly, Sharkey, McGillicuddy, Sheehy.

For one year I took a room in a house by the Heath but something happened, a fractional divisive incident, and I left.

But the Heath remained my Etruscan patera—the saucer representing eternal continuity in the hands of effigies on Etruscan sarcophagi—and this spring, knowing I had to move again, I frequented it more than ever.

Looked at the white hawthorn, red and mauve on the petals with a custard pungency inside. The sweet violets with forks of deeper colour coming out of a dawn-like evanescence in the centre. Bluebells with stripes inside like those on awnings or on Sienese heraldry, insects running inside them. Near the War Memorial a bed of purple pansies with deep yellow spots on one side of the centre and pale yellow crescents on the other.

Became acquainted with the crested greve on one of the ponds, fork of his head, amber at the back of his head, ruff at neck.

Since March swam out to the coots' nest in a lifebuoy on the Men's Pond where the young were hatching.

Two swans came to live on the Men's Pond.

Perhaps because it was coming towards the D-Day anniversary, my landlady for twelve years, pepper-salt hair, in a pinafore with hankie in the breast pocket, borders to the pinafore, under a photograph of Princess Elizabeth, 1929, took out family photographs. She was the only girl in a South London family of boys.

149

The older boys, crinkled hair—Marcel waves—of the thirties. 'Friday night is Amami night,' we used say, stressing the exaltation of shampoo. A tie with stripes going horizontally on the knot and vertically otherwise. White shirts with sleeves in twisted rolls.

Four of the brothers were killed in the war.

She served in the Women's Royal Naval Service in Trincomalee in North East Ceylon.

But she was in South London for VE-Day celebrations. Long tables in the open air, benches; Union Jacks hanging from windows, paper chains between houses, cut-out paper bells above the tables, flowers in jugs, incongruously some of the women in cloche hats and some of the little girls in winter caps, a boy staring at the camera—displaying his legs in long, dark stockings with lines of jonquil brightness in them, my landlady also staring at the camera, in a leopardskin coat with epaulettes and black sleeves.

A trip with a surviving brother in the nineteen-fifties from Victoria to Seattle, on a ship under Golden Lion Bridge, the man's hair seduced in Eastman colour to henna, the flag of Canada with its cherry maple leaf blowing.

By the sea with the same brother, his hair crescendo curled from the right side, in spectator shoes, black and white, with two bars of black going through the white in the middle, advertisements for Wills' Capstan and Walls' Ice-cream and Brooke Bond tea.

Later that day I passed a black wedding party in a front garden in Lewisham Way, a black woman in an apricot dress, black net over her face, looking towards the bus, another woman with a string of petals in her hair, another with silver pea-pods in her hair.

Although it was the beginning of summer I thought of South East London at the end of summer, black mustard growing in waste under huge graffiti 'Maggie's Dream', black girls pushing British Rail trolleys through the grass.

Today I find no clue, no lead on a room in Amsterdam and I go into a café with brown armchairs with very low seats and lamps with brown lampshades, the kind the girl I came to Amsterdam with years ago and I would have gone to.

Lamplight partly lights up a Rembrandt poster on the wall, a Jewish wedding, the ring on the first finger of the girl's right hand showing it's a Jewish wedding. I see my face in a mirror, grey at the edges of my hair the way there's brown on the edges of the camellia flower.

The face of the girl from Galway I knew years ago comes back too, Jewish peoths, inspired by Amsterdam, on either side of her face. Recently in London I met a boyfriend of hers from Galway, who's had lots of breakdowns—once very beautiful, now his curly hair gone grey but his face still young and rosy like pinks in a countrywoman's lapel. He's taking a course in the University of London. And he says he's happy.

Outside again, in the late afternoon sunshine, a wedding party goes by on a barge, old ladies in crimplene seated in a line, young men standing, singing 'Champagna. Champagna.'

I take the train to Zandfoort aan Zee, passing a blue circus tent with auric stars on it.

'Nec mihi Dulichium domus est Ithaceve Samosve . . . My home is not Dulichium or Ithaca or Samos.'

The windows of Zandfoort aan Zee are crowded with sea things—swans with shells at their rear, ships with sails of shells, a Chinese boy in a romper suit, a pear of hair on his bald head, sitting on an amber fish, holding up a lamp: an old Chinese woman kisses the nude breast of a young Chinese woman in the middle of this jumble, a ceramic cat peeps out of a ceramic giftbox, there's a flowering cactus in a pig. Inside one window I see a table, a small bible at each place.

On the beach are shells—saffron and white, white with indigo lines, pure white.

A man in a rose-scarlet shirt goes by in a trotter drawn by a horse, just alongside the waves.

I am in another place, Iowa, an Amish couple in a buggy against the September corn, the man in a pork pie hat, the woman in a poke bonnet.

An old man, just back from Eastern Europe, on a boat on the Mississippi, head in hands, the wispish hair which covered his head albino-white, the American flag blowing, yellow leaves on the boat.

A group photograph by a picture window against the corn-fields. A Chinese woman in a melon-red stole with tassels, big loops of glasses, bent over laughing, a taciturn boy with guinea gold hair beside her.

The gargantuan apartment block in which I stayed by the corn, dozens and dozens of apartments which looked uniform outside but inside had cabinets of crockery with papaya roses inside. We used to have feasts and conversations there.

London, South East London, where I moved after Iowa, has always been lonely for me. Loneliness needs to be dissolved in me, my life needs to be soldered again with a community.

There was six months in Berlin, a feast in May with a German boy who frequently visited me in South East London and who was to die a little over a month later of AIDS—gingerbread, dessert apricots, biscuits from a tin with a goldfish bowl on it—the buildings of Kreuzberg amber in the sunset.

A few months before he died he went to Amsterdam and bought a shirt which had patterns based on a scarf in a William van Vlite painting, red maple leaves.

'And it came to pass, when he made an end to speaking unto Saul, that the soul of Jonathan was knit with the soul of David, and Jonathan loved him as his own soul.'

The old man on the boat was to see me during a trip to Berlin but he died at O'Hare Airport in Chicago.

' . . . Then a boat up the Rhine, Bonn–Mainz, where my one remaining German relative will meet us and for five days we will drive around the Black Forest and visit the small town from which my ancestors emigrated to America.'

It was as if Iowa and Berlin were gilded into one another like parts of a mirror in a Victorian pub, a mirror with a cornucopia back-painted onto it or maybe pomegranates.

But this mirror—mirrors—reflected the cornfields of Iowa in November and the lime trees of Berlin in May.

In the mirror too is the face of the boy who died of AIDS. Just before he died he looked more composed than ever, pink ochre, circle necked jersey, black nylon hair.

'It's the inner freedom. Lose that and you're dead anyway.'

South East London; Victorian chimneys; a brioche called Sally slung in the small windows of old bakeries; a piebald horse, brown and white, drawing a cart with old fridges on it; old women with globe-like hair-dos and tottering steps on long roads with one magnolia tree where men's tattoos were often the insignia of jails—a chain going down an arm to the wrist, huge keys, firmly barred windows; Irish tramps with psoriasis on their feet; South East London the place of the shibboleth—a sudden spit on the pavement.

But the loneliness, the lack of contact with community.

I must move on now from loneliness and give them back their community intact, without me.

'*But when they persecute you in this city, flee ye into another.*'

When I first came to live in South East London people I'd meet in Iowa or as part of my journey to Iowa would come to visit me, sit by the fire, bring stories of their countries and their cities.

An English boy with a sleeper in his ear, dimple in his chin, who'd worked in community centres for Catholic and Protestant children in Belfast, with whom I'd platonically shared a bed in New York, came with his Jewish fiancée who brought sugar pretzels. My cat Eamon was a tiny kitten then.

That was January.

I'd gone to a party in London that Christmas with my friend from Germany, in a cardigan that was the colour of the night sea off Palestine.

The previous September, before I'd moved in here, just after the Sabra and Chatila massacres, I'd been to Israel, resolved myself in the electric blue September light, saw a group of girls on horses go by on the sands, under palm trees, at the Mediterranean near Tel Aviv.

When I returned from Israel and moved into the little flat there was at first a sense of the cornfields of Iowa merging into the place, the way mirrors in a Victorian pub overlap, are gilded onto one another. Then the visitors stopped coming.

A woman from Ireland, chestnut haired, exiled in London, came in a hobble skirt and in a wide brimmed hat with chick feathers on it my first Christmas here and called the food 'beauteous'. That was the night my young friend arrived from Germany. He returned again and again, replacing the people I'd met in Iowa.

And I, as though by covenant, managed to be close to him when he was dying his young and very painful death.

Alone against the Mediterranean I am again—the walled city of Acca, a tight fistful of stars over the sea, areca palms near the port, voices in the dark streets—fighting Ireland—family, fighting England—incipient denigration. Fighting for survival of 'the inner freedom', fighting to exist.

The sunset is gone now and the man in the trotter and Iowa and Israel. The journey is a dead-end. There is no country. My only country is the flag of postcards on the wall—wherever that may happen to be.

But the patera, the continuity goes on, Hampstead Heath, Zandfort aan Zee, the cornfields of Iowa; a walk into a November sunset with the American flag and a flag with the wild rose of Iowa blowing over pumpkins and a look back onto a house, where someone has just sung 'My Tennessee Mountain Home', flaring like someone pulling a cigarette in the night—one of life's few houses of friendship.

A Great Uprooting

ELEANOR FLEGG

The shock of displacement runs, like electric wiring, under the plaster-work that holds our family together. The memory of a wild flight to Moscow and back again. The three of us have landed, winded and a little bruised, in the Kingdom of Fife. Our house has taken us, cradled, into its arms. There was a time when we did not have a place to live.

We started to move, driven by unemployment and a native restlessness. We had imagined ourselves a brave and adventurous family, trekking across the tundra with an infant wrapped in a furred package. But our fine plans foundered and we became disorientated. Circling in the teeth of a rising panic we could not find a place to land. Then I knew what a house says to the people who make their home in it. It comes up behind you and whispers in your ear: *You have a life. You are a family. This is where you are from.* When the home is gone there is only the whistling of the nomad wind.

We began in Dublin. In a bulging, redbrick house where our son was born on a January morning. He slipped out into a pool of water like a little golden fish as the sun rose over the Meath Hospital. The kitchen swung, half built, around his birth. Over a floor swaddled in builders' plastic the newborn father gathered his son into his arms and named him Vanya. From somewhere in the future Russia was reining us in.

The wood stove had burnt low in the long night. The doors were thrown open to warm the newborn Van. The waxy infant safely arrived from the first of his peregrinations. His father, damp from immersion in the birthing tank, made breakfast and stoked the fire. Offering cups of tea, he looked down at his own body and stopped, astonished, in mid sentence. He had come from the water undressed and oblivious to his own nakedness. He covered himself like Adam in the Garden of Eden.

We built the house around the baby. One by one the rooms

155

became habitable. Tif wheeled barrowloads of earth through the sitting room and up a series of planks onto the street outside. In a flight of misguided fancy we garnished the house with organic paint that peeled off the walls in strips in a matter of months. Waxed the wooden floor with beeswax to which the passing earth clung, until the floor became an extension of the back yard. Indistinguishable surfaces of hard packed earth. Eventually we abandoned the environment and hired a man to sand and varnish the wooden floors with a chemical so toxic that we had to vacate the house for a week. We returned to find a pile of letters, embedded in varnish and petrified by the fumes.

As the house took shape around us I cooked for the friends who dropped in. On the way to the pub. On the way home from work. There was always enough to eat, no matter how many people arrived at dinner time. God was working miracles in our kitchen.

We left Dublin in the flight from unemployment and rented a house in the Lowlands of Scotland. A small village under pale wide skies. The weather growled fierce from the North Sea. The child grew, sat in his high chair and scattered porridge into the far corners of the room. He skidded across discarded banana and poured carrot juice into the beige carpeting. Nappiless, he relieved himself at the top of the stairs and then descended. He drew on the walls. He and the dog between them shredded coal, crayons and soft furnishings.

At the time I wondered how could I ever have imagined domesticity to be a constraint. Instead of beeswax embedded with clay we had a quarry tiled kitchen floor. I developed a new and loving relationship with cleaning fluids. The range aired white cloth nappies. Heated limitless water. Baked bread. I washed up in water so hot that the dishes dried as soon as they were stacked steaming in the drainer. Two great sinkfuls of hot water, soapy and clean. A house with a generous heart.

One morning I scrubbed the kitchen in anticipation of a visit. The visits were rarer and more formal than they had been in Dublin. I missed the sound of the doorbell. The endless roundsof tea. Kitchen put in order, I sat down at the computer for a quick half hour before my friend arrived. She looked admiringly around the room. Isn't it wonderful how you can just ignore the housework and get on with your writing.

Our dog was a foundling from Dundee. A little yellow lurcher with amber eyes. Her name was Willow. I had been longing for her for months before I found her, and I knew her instantly. She was waiting in kennel number ten, between two big barking Alsatians. She lay very still in my arms on the way back, curled nose to tail like a fawn. I never dreamed that she would be so fast.

She ran like a slip of the wind. Vanished for hours at a time. Chased anything that moved; rolled in anything that smelt. A wee gurrier from Dundee. We walked for hours in the woods above the house. Vanya slept in the backpack, his nose bumping off my shoulder. We saw the seasons turn. The winter birch trees scratched the sky like purple lace. Their skin was as silvery gold as the dog's fur. The arms of the larches filled up with snow. They pointed towards Russia.

Everything pointed towards Russia: dreams, qualifications, abilities. The future stopped short beneath our feet. It was a great uprooting.

We left the Scottish village and bought tickets for Moscow. Everything was dismantled and the ends sealed up. I felt dazed, as though this was happening to somebody else. Our home was being torn limb from limb. My sense of myself was dismantled and packed up small. Willow went to live with a friend in Glasgow. Now there were just three of us and the open road.

On the first evening in Moscow I went up onto the steep pitched roof across which live wires ran down into the apartments below. The red stars of the Kremlin glowed. A ring of fireworks rose up in a circle around the city and the roof dropped wildly from under my feet. The fireworks lifted again into the heavy dusk. Solzenitzyn had come home.

This was old Moscow. Unexpectedly pretty. The buildings were crumbling wedding cakes in white and pink. Lenin lay like a waxwork in his tomb and the Moscow river boiled beneath vast bridges. Outside the old heart of the city Stalin's tower blocks rose in a grey ring. Tif walked the streets with all his hopes alight. He swam like a fish in the murky Moscow water. Looked Russian, spoke Russian. It was his great dream.

I waited long days to catch up with myself, appalled by a churlishness that I tried to conceal. I felt that I had been hollowed out, like an Easter egg. A light, sweet, chocolate shell. How long were we to stay? Ten years he said. Three months. In the winter we can go south to the Black Sea. Across the border into Turkey. Nobody can stand the Moscow winter.

Where will we live? Here. A safe haven in the Russian wilderness. The Russian family with whom we stayed had opened their house to us. It was like an apartment in a dream. Nine high white rooms flowing with artists, poets and musicians. People coming in from the street with bread, fruit and flowers gleaned from the changing city markets. But this family, their warmth and creativity enfolding us, how long did they expect us to stay? Did they mind? Were we welcome? I could not read between the lines of a foreign language. And here was I, the seasoned traveller, suddenly devastated, uprooted and beset by an increasing numbness. An inability to find my place. I was feeling my way through a thickening fog.

I walked the streets open handed and was not cheated. My stuttering progress was met with a patience that I had not expected. And still I was disorientated. I was homesick for the wide Fife skies. For our home. We could not afford a place of our own in Moscow. The rents were prohibitive, and it seemed so ungrateful, having been offered so much, to turn around and say that we needed our own place. But it was important. More important than anything else. I felt that we had lost our place in the world and were now hurtling through space. Our time in Russia was endless and bottomless. We had left nothing to come back to.

And Vanya, named for Russia, took flight of his own accord and landed on the broken teeth of a Russian playground. It was a Soviet playground. A forest of metal stumps set into hard-packed earth. A climbing frame ceaselessly guarded by a feral child. A swing that flung high and angled from the rusting frame. It was from this swing that our son cast himself into mid air. He landed on hard earth and broken metal.

The severed lap of his nostril rose and fell with his breath. We took him to the hospital and waited with him in our arms. The corridor was empty. From the far end three Russian nurses came towards us, huge as battleships. They took him from us. His cry rose like a warning siren. We followed. Were expelled back into the empty corridor. I saw them lay him down on a table, needles flashing. He was putting up a brave fight. The door was closed between us and his continuous scream. We waited. The screams got louder and louder and then stopped. We could hear nothing. I stood out in the street in the pouring rain.

Returned, drenched, to find Vanya restored, bruised and shaken, to his father's knee. His nose sewed tightly back in its proper place and painted green like the nose of a little clown.

His father held him proudly. 'He didn't tell them *anything*!'

The green ointment was called *zillionka*. Zillion green. A bright, circus colour. I thought that we had arrived in a land where colours had power of remedy. Old fashioned stains. Iodine. Gentian violet. Mercuric Iodide.

We were immured in the apartment. Following the hospital visit Vanya had coughed, flagged and not recovered his high spirits. None of the local remedies had diverted his illness. He had a criss cross pattern of iodine painted onto his back. A mustard compress on his chest. Burnt sugar to suck. Vodka on his forehead and garlic on the soles of his feet.

In spite of all these curatives he broke out in spots. This time the doctor came up to the apartment. *Vitrianka*, she said, and gave us another bottle of green ointment. With the aid of a dictionary we worked out that it was chicken pox. Mild but uncomfortable. Each spot was to be painted daily with green. This as well as the usual hygienic excavation of the nose on which the doctors had done a good job; it was sewn on tight as tight could be. Owing to the number of spots and the slipperiness of the child I thought that we might be better to paint him all over and forget about the individual spots. The ointment stained clothing, furnishing, floors and walls.

I was not the pioneer I had imagined, to keep my nerve in a foreign apartment with a fretful Van. No amount of kindness could fill my need for a place of our own. And so I fled, my green son under my arm and the Russian dream shattering in my wake. I came back to Ireland. In terms of orientation, it was a start.

from A Little Girl, Never Out Before

CLARE BOYLAN

The little girl sat on the edge of the bed in the dark, her blanket wrapped around her shoulder, her bare legs dangling over the edge. Unknown to sun or sky, it was morning. She had slept a little towards dawn, a dizzy sickly doze, and then woken in a panic because the baby was missing. She always slept with it in her arms and they woke up wet but warm. In the day she carried the infant while she cleaned up or cooked and her hands were formed to its support.

When she opened her eyes she thought she was at home because of the loud, gurgling snores that were like her da's but it was Lena. Lena was who she lived with now. She wondered when she'd ever see her ma again, or cuddle the baby. Ah, she missed her ma. She cried for a few minutes, wiping her eyes and nose with her blanket, but Lena reached out her big knobby foot and gave her a kick so she pulled on her brown pinafore and her stockings and boots and went down to light the range.

Her room was in the attic of the house and she crept down its five storeys in the dark, past the snuffling creaking married couples, past the yearning schoolteacher and the long-faced woman with the opossum cape, past the dark dining room and drawing room which waited in silence to claim life from her fidgeting hands.

The cold possessed her like a drowning. She felt her way to the kitchen and stood there in the dark. Lena had not shown her where to find matches. Who can tell what hides in the dark of old kitchens, scuttling about with mice and mould and skins of dripping? The sounds that live inside total silence are the worst in the world. She crept around, her fingers touching things that felt horrible— soaking porridge, tea leaves in a sieve. Her breath came out in persevering grunts. At last she grasped a match and lit the kitchen lamp. It leaked a little pool of yellow light and monsters swarmed up the wall. She knelt on the floor and began to rake out the ashes.

It was her mother's idea that she should go to work in a big house. They were pals. They comforted each other with sweet tea and the flesh of babies. Her da was always after her ma, all the time. They could have stopped him, disabled him with a knife or a chair, but they had a weakness. They both loved infants, newborn. No matter that there wasn't enough for the existing ones to eat, Frankie and her ma saw infants as the marvel of the world. It was worth all the hurting and the hunger to have another, brand new, every other year.

They were a hopeless pair, she and her ma. When her father had gone out for the day and the middle ones were in school Frankie would climb back into bed beside her. They kept themselves warm with the two little ones. They dreamed of the feasts they might eat if there was ever any money, but they didn't bother all that much. Hunger was just a fact of their life, and there were rewards.

It was after Frankie got her women's monthlies that the notion arose of sending her away. She was growing into a lady now, her ma said. It was time to learn a lady's life.

Her ma said that she would learn the quality of fine silver and how to stitch linen. She would eat blancmange and cold beef in the kitchen. She would gather roses in a wicker basket and arrange them on a polished table by a long window. It became their new dream, after the dreams of food. In idle fancy they walked under wedding-cake ceilings, exploring the rooms, peeking into bureaux to spy on love letters, opening the lids of golden boxes to admire jewels or bon bons or cigars inside. They mooned over the young man of the house who was kind but distant, concealing emotion beneath a brittle moustache as he played at the piano.

She didn't look any more like a lady than she had the year before. Her legs were sticks and her chest was flat as a wash board. All the same she was growing up and her father knew it too. Sometimes when he came in from his night's drinking and had performed gravely in the bucket in the corner, he would reach not for Ma but for Frankie, his dimmed senses directed by nostalgia to the spring scent of womanhood and not its spent season.

She stuffed the stove's ugly gob with coke and papers and stood over it while it lit, shivering and warming her legs as she tempted it with morsels of twisted paper and a sprinkling of sugar the way her mother had shown her. By the time it was lighting the kitchen clock said a quarter past seven and she had to run to catch up. There was no time to wash her hands when she finished the fires so that the breakfast plates and saucers were branded by her black prints as she set the tables.

In all their uncertain fantasies of grandeur the one thing Frankie and her ma had been sure of was that there would be enough to eat in a big house. Poor ma wouldn't believe it if she told her she had nothing since her tea yesterday, which was two slices of the sour brown bread smeared with marge. There would be no more until after the boarders had eaten breakfast, when she could have some of the porridge that remained.

The poor learn to live with hunger by moving slowly and sleeping a lot but she had hardly slept and she had to run all the time to keep up with the work. As she set out the bread and sausages and rings of black pudding for Lena to cook for breakfast, her fingers fell to temptation and stealthily fed her a slice of bread. After that she went upstairs to knock up the married couples.

Mrs Deveney was pleased with the little girl's first day. She wasn't sociable. She did not look at the male boarders nor loiter on the landings with Lena. In spite of her dreamy air, she was thorough. Her fires did not go out. An inspection of the dishes she washed revealed no scabs of oatmeal, no rusty stains of tea. She summoned Frankie after she had finished making the beds and emptying the slops. The child looked dazed. Her face was a panic-stricken white and her hands black as the devil. 'What are you?' Mrs Deveney asked her briskly.

'I'm a girl.' Frankie looked surprised. 'A maid.' She knew nothing. She had answered wrong. She waited patiently while the lupin lips wove themselves into a shape for contumely.

'You are a filthy, thieving little tinker of the common lower orders,' Mrs Deveney said.

Frankie looked at the big black piano, as fat and listless as a funeral horse. She wondered if the boarders ever dared to use it, if one of the silent men at breakfast might serenade his new wife, while she leaned across the lid to show him her breasts.

Oft in the stilly night . . . Her mother used to sing that long ago. She wondered what her ma was doing now. Was the baby fretting for her?

'Look at me!' snapped Mrs Deveney. 'Explain yourself.'

A bag of bones her da used to say, until she began to turn into a lady. A flock of dreams. A waking ghost. A gnaw of hunger.

'You left filthy black fingerprints all over the breakfast china and you stole a slice of bread.'

'I was hungry,' Frankie said, and then, invaded by curiosity: 'how did you know?'

'The nerve of you! Every stim in this house is counted. The bread is cut the night before—two slices for every boarder. It was Lena who informed me of the robbery.'

Mrs Deveney demanded to know why Frankie had not worn gloves while doing the dirty work of the house, the grates and the slops, and declared that she had brought a breath of depravity into a good Catholic household. She believed it too but did not add that it was a matter of routine. All the servants stole. She expected it and kept their rations meagre knowing that thieving was in their nature and that they would steal food whether they needed it or not.

In a matter of weeks Frankie would grow cunning and learn to conceal evidence of her enterprise. Lena was by now an accomplished bandit. Search as she might Mrs Deveney could only find clues to modest pilferage yet the girl grew fatter by the hour.

Was ever a slice of bread so richly mourned? The little salt-spoon eyes seemed to corrode yet further as rebuke buzzed from the withered lips. And still she was hungry. She thought about the newest baby, Doris, whose eyes were not like salt spoons but like measured sips of a morning sky. At first those eyes had been blind and it was her little ruched mouth that pondered but in a little while everything was lit up by their wonder as if they saw the face of God, if you believed in that sort of thing, or a fairy.

Jack was next, named by their father after the boxer Jack Kilraine, the Terror of the Age, but their Jack was only two and had not yet fulfilled his father's hopes, having a preference for sweetened milk and women's bodies. There was Ethel and Mick, aged six and ten. Frankie loved them all and felt gratified by their need of her. She was proud to be her mother's protector. She had no desire for an independent life. Her own needed her. They always would. She thought of them all alone, with no one to comfort them or cook for them, and panic gripped at her knees. Who would cheer her ma up in the morning after her da had gone, leaving the trail of his temper, a smell of beer and the dank aftermath of his night-time business?

She always lay on the bed looking cold and sort of grey until Frankie brought her tea and opened the windows and sang a few songs and lit up the ashes in the grate.

Christmas was only six weeks off and the small ones were already counting. Frankie was the one who made the ginger biscuits and scrounged for oranges to put in the children's stockings. It was she who saved up new pennies, one for each child.

'I'm going home now,' she said in her offhand way. 'My ma will be wanting me.'

'Ah, now,' the widow looked alarmed. 'Your mammy is depending on the few shillings. You'd only be letting her down.'

'No I wouldn't,' Frankie said. 'My ma loves me.'

'Of course she does,' Mrs Deveney forced her mouth down into a smile. 'You're only in want of refinement and religion. You should pin your hair up and maybe I'd make you a present of a gown for Sundays. Bríd Feeney's grey could be cut down for you. I'm going to give you time off to go to Mass and confession with Lena. What do you say?'

Frankie shook her head. She was too tired. She only wanted to go home.

'And if you were loyal to me, of course, you would get a nice present at Christmas—something you could bring home to benefit your poor little brothers and sisters. Say "yes ma'am".' Her smile vanished when she saw ambition enter Frankie's dreamy eye. 'Say "thank you, ma'am".'

She got used to the wearing of household gloves, the smell of chloride of lime and the racking bouts of grief that she carried carefully to the outside lavatory. She learned to steal things that could not be counted, spoons of starch or custard powder, a fistful of dry oatmeal.

The married couples came and went, their honeymoons accomplished with relief, if not much comfort. McMahon the schoolteacher stayed on. Sometimes he invited Frankie into his room, but she said she wasn't allowed. The boys who came to the back door with fish or groceries tried to grapple with her but she was a good kicker. Anyway, they preferred Lena who developed a kind of glamour in the hands of men, allowing them to feel her giant bosoms or anything they liked.

Once she surprised her in the pantry with a bakery lad. The youth and the massive girl turned to gawp at her. 'Get out! Get away you dirty little scut, you cur,' Lena snarled.

'You'll get a baby if you do that,' Frankie told her.

'Don't you be ridiculous,' Lena said. 'How could I get a baby now?'

Frankie laughed, which earned her a blow on the ear. There was no argument to that.

Within a month she had begun to turn into one of those wiry little workers, who are silent and swift and indispensable. Mrs Deveney kept her word and came up the five flights of stairs, carrying, with caution and difficulty, her Christmas gift.

It was a little house or shed. The roof was thatched like those of the poor cottagers who lived in the hills, and animals wandered around inside. A poor little baby slept in a pigsty or something.

'What is it?' Frankie said. She had been hoping for money or a box of biscuits, something for the children.

'It is the holy crib,' Mrs Deveney stood back to let the child peer inside the house where she saw that there were toy people as well as animals and the baby. Foreigners. 'What's it for?' she said.

'It is to put you in mind of the spirit of Christmas,' the widow mystifyingly declared. 'The figure in the manger is baby Jesus and the lady in blue is His mother, the Virgin Mary.'

'She can't be His mother,' Frankie said; 'not if she's a virgin.'

'These are the three wise kings, led to Bethlehem by a star shining from the East, who came to worship and brought gold, frankincense and myrrh.'

'Who were they?' Frankie wondered.

'They were gifts!' Mrs Deveney tried to hide her impatience of the little girl's stupidity, for it was all as plain to her as right and wrong, but her teeth clenched and she sprayed spit. 'Gifts of inestimable value. Lena will explain.'

But all Lena explained was that Jesus Mary and Joseph they had enough junk in the room already. She picked up the little house just as little Frankie was examining a mouse-sized ox. She climbed on to her own bed and heaved the crib up on top of the wardrobe.

How To Be Irish In London

JOSEPH O'CONNOR

It was a pretty interesting time to live over there, because the Queen wasn't the only Londoner having problems. A few nights after the day I saw her, I was on my way home from a party, when a strange and memorable thing happened to me. I was standing on the platform at Charing Cross Station when I saw a young man that I thought I recognised. He reminded me of my brother, actually. He had the same build, the same haircut. I approached this young man. I was curious about him. I got up very close beside him. Then I could see that his clothes were shabby. His face was grey, the colour of porridge. I knew then that he was not my brother. I knew he was a homeless person.

Suddenly he fell forwards onto the platform, his arms flailing. People did nothing at all about this. People raised their newspapers to their eyes. He seemed to roll forwards a little, so that he almost fell down onto the track. After a moment, two young women approached him. I went to help them get him up on his feet. We got him up, and he started moaning with pain. We brought him out to the street, and then the two women went away.

I gave him some money for a cup of tea. I wanted to get away from him, I am ashamed to say. I wanted him to take the money and leave me alone, but he looked up at me then. 'Would you be able to come with me?' he said. He was Irish. He just wanted someone to go for a cup of tea with him.

We walked up Saint Martin's Lane to a late night coffee place near Leicester Square. We got some tea, and he ate a bit of soggy toast. He had a very bad cough. He kept wincing in pain whenever he coughed. He was shaking badly.

He was from Athlone, he said. He'd had a bad row with his father. His mother had run off somewhere, and his father's girl-friend had moved into the house, and there had been rows. He had been beaten up by his father, and he'd had to get away. He hadn't been in London for long.

We talked a bit about Irish music. He liked the band Something Happens, he told me, he had seen them play a few times. He kept shuddering and shaking and coughing. He hadn't eaten anything at all in a few days, he said.

He asked me what I did for a living, and I told him I wrote books, and that sometimes I wrote for newspapers. Which ones?, he wanted to know. *The Sunday Tribune* was one, I said. He nodded. He'd sometimes read *The Sunday Tribune*, he told me, and he liked it. He took another sip of the hot tea, and his hands trembled again. Did I know Paul Kimmage, *The Sunday Tribune* sports reporter? No, I told him, I didn't. That was a pity, he said. Paul Kimmage wrote great articles in *The Sunday Tribune*.

I tried to ask him about his life in London. It was the loneliness that would get you, he said, rather than the cold or the hunger. It wasn't the begging, or the way you had to shit into plastic bags, because they wouldn't even let you into the pubs to use the toilet. It was waking up in a doorway at six in the morning, freezing cold, and knowing that you wouldn't talk to a single person all day long. He said it a was terrible thing to wake up by yourself, in your filthy clothes, and to know you'd have to walk around all day, until it was time to go to sleep in a doorway again.

I tried to give him more money, but he didn't want to take it. I insisted, and in the end he took it. Then a terrible thing happened. Suddenly, his face crumpled up and he started to cry. He started to sob, the way a child would. His face screwed up and he hung his head and wept. I put my hand on the back of his wrist and he grabbed my hand and squeezed it hard, still crying, without looking at me. I was very close to crying myself. He said he just didn't know what he was going to do. He kept looking around himself, with a look of utter confusion and fear in his face. 'I'm only hanging on by my laces,' he kept saying. Hanging on by my laces. He was about the same age as me. He was absolutely despairing.

Our so-called leaders should know that any night of the week you will find young people from every corner of our country, over in London, all hanging on by their laces in a city where they're treated like scum. They are hungry and cold. They have absolutely nothing. Our political leaders should think a bit about this, while they're discussing their beautiful options with each other.

He was from Athlone, he said. His second name was Foley. He asked me, next time I wrote anything in *The Sunday Tribune*, to put in the paper that he was alright, that he was making out OK in London, and that he said hello to anyone in Ireland who knew him.

One day as I was moseying down Bleeker Street in downtown Manhattan, honest to God, a homeless man wearing nothing but his underpants and a pair of boxing boots jumped out in front of me, tapped me on the shoulder and pointed up at the sky. 'Jeez, dude,' he cried, breathily, 'check *that* out.' 'What?,' I said. He nudged me hard in the ribs. '*Look*,' he insisted. 'Look up, man. Is it a bird? Is it a plane?'

'I don't know,' I said. He pulled a lipstick out of his trunks, quickly scrawled a large 'S' on his chest, then held out his hand to me, beaming. 'No, it's Superwino, man! Now gimme a greenback.'

Over in London, the poor were not quite as creative, although their plight was just as scandalous. (In London, for example, homeless people are twenty times more likely to be sexually assaulted or murdered than other members of the public.)

One night, anyway, I went to review 'Sunset Boulevard' for *The Sunday Tribune*. The theatre is in the Strand, an opulent part of the city, and the audience seemed to be very rich. Certainly, there was a long line of limos outside, the like of which you would not even see in Charlie Haughey's driveway. And after the play, as the limos roared off, the homeless people were huddled in the doorways all along the Strand, wrapping themselves in newspapers and polythene bags, trying to stay out of the rain.

I was just wandering along the street by myself, trying to think of what I would say about 'Sunset Boulevard' in the paper the next Sunday when a middle-aged woman came up to me with a baby in her arms. She handed me a note. 'I am refugee of Bosnia. Help me. All my family are killed in Sarajevo.'

Well, I felt sorry for this woman. Anyone who lives in London gets to know pretty quickly when people really are poor. There's a desperation in the face, an awful darkness behind the eyes. It's a thing actors never get right. When people are utterly poor they do not look excited. They look hopeless and frightened and half-dead, the way this unfortunate woman looked.

I patted my pockets furiously but had no change. I had spent every last bob on purchasing a large gin and tonic at half time. With anything written by Andrew Lloyd Webber, I find, you do tend to need chemical stimulation if you want to last until the final curtain. I was embarrassed that I couldn't help. I apologised and went to walk on. She reached into her pocket and handed me another note. 'I have nowhere to sleep and my child is hungry.'

I didn't know what to do. So I told her about this hostel I knew for homeless people, where a girl I knew used to work. She didn't seem to get what I was saying, although gradually I formed the odd impression that she did understand, but was pretending not to. I took out a pen and drew a map for her, on the back of her note, indicating the whereabouts of this hostel. And I walked on.

The Bosnian woman began to walk alongside me, staring at me all the time. As I quickened my pace, she broke into a trot. I began to get a little uptight. And she began to run along beside me then, panting and coughing, chattering away in what I presumed was the Bosnian language. Suddenly, she thrust out her hand and grabbed my lapel. 'Look,' I said. 'I'd love to help you but I really have no money. I'm sorry.' And then a strange thing happened. She stepped back from me, this Bosnian lady, and put one hand on her hip. Her upper lip curled into a sneer. 'Ah would you fuck off with yourself,' she exclaimed, 'sure you're only a fucker anyway.' A telling moment.

She was from Dublin, this poor woman. But she was pretending to be a Bosnian refugee, so that she could beg enough money to eat.

Grow a Mermaid

MARINA CARR

The child leaned across the blue formica table and read the advertisement, her grubby little fingers leaving snail tracks under the words—GROW YOUR OWN MERMAID.

The child looked at the words in amazement, read it again, slowly, more carefully this time. The same. Underneath the caption was an ink drawing of a tiny mermaid in a fish bowl, waving and smiling up from the page. Behind her was a sea-horse. He too was smiling. The child, bewitched by the mermaid's smile, smiled back and waved shyly to the tiny beautiful fish woman. Send 25 cents, the advertisement said, and we will send you mermaid and sea-horse seeds. You put them into water and they grow and can even talk to you. The child imagined waking up at night and going to the fishbowl for a little chat with the mermaid. What would mermaids talk about, the child wondered.

The child's mother stirred beans in a pot over the cooker, her black corseted behind moving in one controlled sway with the spooning motion. Over by the range Grandma Blaize was fossicking for some long forgotten thing. She was pulling it out of the air above her head with her fingertips. The child looked at her and then the child's mother turned to watch as well, still stirring the beans, sideways now. Both mother and child watched as Grandma Blaize pulled some invisible treasure to earth. She saw them looking at her and gave them a quick smile, a dart of old gums and leathery tongue, before her face took up that careful concentration of fossicking and pulling again.

'Ara stop it Grandma Blaize!' the child's mother snapped.

Grandma Blaize ignored her. Tonight or tomorrow she'll have stepped into the other world. Once the fossicking started she was on the descent. The child liked her best at this point, the moment before going down. The child imagined that Grandma Blaize was pulling open a door with a magic thread, a door on somewhere else, anywhere but away from here.

'Mom look,' the child said, holding up the picture of the mermaid. The mother left off stirring the beans and came over to the child.

'Oh that,' she said, glancing at the magazine the child was reading.

'Grow your own mermaid,' the mother read. 'Did you ever . . .'

Her voice trailed off as she too was bewitched by the little mermaid smiling and waving from her fish bowl.

'Well I never heard the likes o' that,' the mother said, sort of dismayed, but still looking at the mermaid.

'Can we Mom?' the child asked.

'Can we what?'

'Can we send away for a mermaid?'

'We'll see.' Her mother sighed and returned to the burning beans.

The child's mother was building a house on the lake of the palaces. From the end of the field of their own house they could look across and see the new house. It was halfway there now. The child's mother said it was a secret. The child wasn't to tell any of the Connemara clique because they'd wonder where the money came from. The money was borrowed from four banks, the child's mother whispered, and when your daddy sees this house he'll fall in love with it, especially the music room, and he'll come back, for good this time. Some nights they'd talk for hours about how they'd decorate the house. 'Windows, windows everywhere,' the child's mother whispered in the dark. They slept together a lot since the child's father had gone. 'And your room,' the child's mother whispered, 'will be all in yellow, with a yellow sink and yellow curtains, yellow presses and a yellow carpet.' The child didn't like yellow but said nothing. She wanted her room blue and green, like a mermaid's room. It didn't matter, she'd pull blue and green from an invisible string, the way Grandma Blaize did, and then the mermaid would arrive. Some nights the child's mother held the child so tight she couldn't breathe. The child grew sticky and hot as her mother whispered into the quilt about 'that bastard!' and 'all I've done for him' and 'this is how he repays me'. The child would try to put her hand outside the covers to get a bit of cool air on it and the child's mother would grab it and pull it back into the slick heat of the bed. 'My little darling,' the child's mother would croon as the child lay there soaked in sweat, with her mother's damp face on her neck. The child fought back a scream. Down the hall Grandma Blaize sang 'The Connemara Lullaby'; she was in the other world now and would speak to no-one but herself until the end of spring. The child lay there in the dark, growing a mermaid.

First the water from the lake of the palaces, then a Tupperware box, then pour in the mermaid seeds and stir it all gently and the next day a mermaid would be floating on her back, smiling at the child. And the child would say, 'Hello little mermaid'. And the mermaid would sing a song for the child about the sea, about castles and whales and turtles and whole cities and families who lived under the sea. And the child would tell the mermaid all about school and her friend Martina, who played with her sometimes, and about the time they saw a balloon in the sky and chased it for hours. The child would tell her about Pollonio, the fairy she never saw, but knew lived down Mohia Lane. To make it more interesting for the mermaid, the child would pretend that she often met Pollonio. The child slept as the mermaid grew away out in the dark at the edge of the child's dream.

Grandma Blaize lay in bed fighting with the ghost of Syracuse. Propped by pillows, pulling on an opium pipe, she snarled at the ghost of Syracuse. 'Gorgin' ya'ar gut was all y'ever done, ya stroinseach ya!' She takes another puff to calm herself down after this exertion. The ghost of Syracuse was the husband who stepped out the door one day 'to get a breath of fresh air' and never came back. That was thirty years ago. The child watched through the keyhole. He'd sent her a postcard from Syracuse, 'Weather lovely, skies purple most every night, try it sometime.' Grandma Blaize had it covered in plastic and punched it at regular intervals. The child rocked with laughter and banged her nose on the doorknob.

The child ate sweets belonging to her sick brother and the child's mother ordered the child into the black and red parlour. The child waited. After what seemed forever the child's mother appeared in the doorway with a wooden hanger.

'Now strip,' the child's mother said and watched while the child took off everything. Afterwards, lying on the sofa with welts as big as carrots on her legs, the child slept and dreamt of a man with a pitchfork who lived under the sea. 'How long?' the child whispered.

'Soon, soon,' the man with the pitchfork answered. The child woke to find her mother standing over her. 'Have you anythin' to say to me?'

'Sorry Mom.' It was an ancient ritual between them.

'And you'll never do it again?'

The child wavered, looked away.

'Will you?' the mother said, a whiff of anger coming off her that would re-ignite given the least excuse.

'No,' the child half-yielded but it wasn't enough to appease, the child could sense. Her mother was insurmountable in this mood and the child valued the unwelted slivers of her chubby torso. The child surrendered. 'No, never again.'

The child's mother gathered her up in her fat still young arms. The child counted her breaths, slowly, carefully. They matched her mother's footsteps on the stairs. A mermaid would die in this house, the child thought.

The child's father returned and magicked the nuts out of their ears and made pennies hop. One evening he came in, wearing his big blue crombie and sat the child's brother on the blue formica table.

'I can make you disappear,' the child's father said.

The child's brother puffed out his little chest, delighted to be the chosen one. The child watched, wishing it was her.

'The only problem is,' the child's father said, 'you can never come back.'

The child's brother's face crumpled up as he began to cry.

'It's all right,' the child's father said, 'I won't make you disappear.'

The child's brother still cried, ashamed he was crying in front of his father and his little sister.

'It's all right,' the father said, 'I won't do it.'

The child stepped forward.

'Make me disappear,' the child said.

'You can't come back.'

'I don't want to,' the child said.

The child's father shook. 'You're too young for this trick.' The child's father left the room. The child took her brother's hand.

'Come on around the back and play where Mom and Dad's not looking.'

The child's brother allowed himself to be led from the house, his tears forgotten, his childish dignity returning. They played in the ash pit and drank water from the kitchen drain. It tasted of turnip and tea leaves. They weren't caught that time.

The child got up on Sam Morrison's tractor one day with her brother and her mother and Grandma Blaize who was fighting with herself on top of the dresser. The child's father lifted her up on to the trailer and put her on the black sofa. The child's mother laughed. She wore a new dress and a new hair clasp for her thick dark hair. They drove down the lane and stopped outside the new house at the lake of the palaces. A swan glided by, a pike leaped, the mermaid sang.

The child's father went away again, in the middle of the night this time. The child's mother knocked the child's brother's head through the glass door. The child counted her breaths, sharp and shallow. Her brother looked at her as the child's mother held him while the doctor cleaned the wound.

'It's so hard to watch them,' she whispers at the doctor. The doctor nods. Later the child's mother took them into the Oasis for knickerbocker glories. The jelly was gold and green, the colour of the mermaid's tail.

At night the child dreamt her mother was cooking her on the range and serving her up to the tinkers with homemade bread. The child woke screaming, her mother's boiling hand slobbering over her. The child preferred the nightmare.

Down in the room Grandma Blaize tears a map of Syracuse into a thousand pieces and smokes them in her opium pipe. She throws in the Sea of Galilee for good measure.

The child's mother sits by the window nightly, looking out on the lake of the palaces. The music room is empty. She drinks Paddy and red and kisses her children. The child heaves at her mother's whiskey breath. 'Any day now,' the child's mother whispers. 'Any day now.'

The child's mother walked into the lake of the palaces one calm night with the moon missing. The child's father returned, for good this time. He skulks along the lake shore with his weak old whingy eyes. 'He pisses tears,' the child whispers to the mermaid and they both laugh in the silent house. The child's brother rarely speaks now and never to the child. They exchange glances over banana sandwiches and their father's runaway eyes. They haven't drunk from drains in years, not together anyhow.

When they dragged the lake of the palaces for her mother's body, the child sat in the reeds strumming her tiny guitar. She only knew 'My Darling Clementine'. C.G seventh. C again. *Oh my darling, oh my darling, oh my darling Clementine, dwelt a miner, forty-niner, and his daughter Clementine. Like she was and like a fairy and her shoes were number nine, now she's lost and gone forever, oh my darling Clementine.* The child sang, strumming her small guitar as a pulley raised her mother in the air, then they lowered her till she skimmed along the surface towards the child in the reeds. They didn't stop until her head was resting on a clump of rushes, a few feet from the child. '*Oh my darling . . .*' the child sang.

From the child's vantage point, her mother was not unlike the mermaid, bar the pike teeth-marks on her left arm. They'd tasted her and left her to the eels, the dirtiest eaters of all. But the eels hadn't touched her. Maybe they hadn't time or maybe eels too had their standards, the child thought. She strummed her guitar and looked away from her mother's cold heron stare.

'That's enough, child,' a man in the boat said.

The child sang louder. This was the real funeral. The coffin on tick, the procession, the sanctimonious hymns, the concelebrated Mass would all come soon enough. The Connemara clique there, grabbing on to her with their battered claws and defeated lumpy old backs. The child coughed away a titter of amusement at their mouth of the grave *mhuire strua* antics. She insisted on wearing her blue jeans instead of the black velvet gibble they'd bought her. They never forgave her for that. It wasn't real, none of it. Strumming her tiny guitar in the reeds was, with her mother skimmin' towards her stinkin' of goose scream and the bullin' moon.

The child's father took the child and the child's brother into the dining room.

'In memory of your dear mother . . .' he said, the whinge gaining strength at the back of his craw. The child looked at him in disgust.

'In memory of your dear mother I'm going to remain celibate for six months.'

The child blushed.

'What's that?' the child's brother asked.

The child knew.

'I won't sleep with anyone for six months.'

The child ran from the room. Later the child found a box of magazines in her father's cupboard. All lurid fat women's gees. The child put them under her bed. The next time she looked they were gone. The child knew who had them. That night she tore one of his eyes out in a dream. The next night she sewed it back in.

One by one Grandma Blaize pulls out her teeth. She lays them on her dressing table. They're soft as toffee. The child sucks one. It tastes like old knickers. The child crunches down on it with her own strong white horse's teeth. The tooth slivers like a soft mint. The child spits it in the lake of the palaces and eats a fistful of grass. It tastes of swan's wing.

The child sleeps for twenty years. The mermaid who never came is long forgotten. Walking down a street one day, the child takes off her mother's wedding ring and hurls it in a dustbin.

It disappears among the old chips, cigarette butts, an ice cream cone half-eaten. The child goes home and sleeps.

The child is in a swimming pool. It seems she will never reach the bottom, then she does. A fortress door creaks open, a flash of golden fin, the mermaid appears.

'At last, you've come at last,' the child says.

The mermaid smiles, that smile of years ago at the blue formica table. The child braces herself for the watery descent. The mermaid's tail lights the way.

PART 4

Striding the

Paths of this Parish

Goldsmith Goes Home

JOHN MACKENNA

He settles restlessly,
the twelve good rules fly like bats in the darkness,
whipped from the walls of every alehouse in his past.
He would trade memory for life.
Thigh deep in corn,
pausing on the elbow of a road,
he caught the weight of hawthorn
and knew, in that moment, his ghost would never loiter
    in Westminster
but under a maybush on a wet spring evening,
understanding the language,
little understood.
He smiles to know his words, his heart, his liver will be
analysed.

In life the women upstairs are laughing viciously,
dice rattle on the board
and his brain is racing,
the lines and phrases coming,
the poem like a haemorrhage
from his body swollen and abused,
leaving no room, no energy for living.
He would trade fame for peace.

This city is not real,
his reality is the past;
not London or the steep streets of Edinburgh;
not the Bishop's examination; the legal offices;
the smell of medicine.
He is back, flute in pocket,
on the wet street where children play.

Burke and Reynolds are less real than these skipping
    infants;
the obliging drunken women are the dream,
and the dream of singing hedges is reality.
He would trade pleasure for release.

The edging ship for Leyden or Padua
awakens something momentarily
and out on the ocean
the regular waves
restore the ploughman to the furrow on the field.
Dining finely with Johnson and their lady friends
he turns so suddenly, stopped by laughter,
catching the last tapered echo
of an echo heard at Blackfriars—
faint but certain.
The October wind gathers
the midland smells and voices
and drops them in his sleeping lap
but he awakes to the sound of footsteps on his grave.

He settles restlessly
and the earth closes about the broken machinery of his
    life,
the clay rattles in the space about his bones,
at the corner of his smile.
Free at last, his ghost, a peaceful Heathcliff,
strides the paths of this parish
pausing in the shelter of this tree or this or this.

Home from England

JAMES RYAN

At last the train arrived in what we had, all morning, been calling our station. It was very near the town but so different to any of the buildings in the town that it always looked isolated. We were the only ones to get off the train that afternoon and as we grouped loosely around our luggage, looking out for someone we knew, the place seemed more desolate than ever. There was something disappointing about the way the train shunted out of the station. It was, I suppose, the thought that there were other places to go, making our destination seem just one of many. The event was somehow diminished, and the marching band turned into a small family group pushing three tan suitcases along an empty platform.

I tried to will myself back into the whirl of expectation. But, as I backed away, my other memories of the station poured in. I trailed unwillingly in the wake of those memories, seeing my father on his way back to England—sitting in the front seat of the hackney car leaning forward. His knuckles, always pressed white against the dashboard, while he stared out into the distance where the hedges looped over the road. All that time standing on the platform, and maybe it was only a couple of seconds, I tried to hold out against the thought that no matter how many times or under what circumstances I might arrive in that station the feeling would always be one of defeat.

I rose and sank in quick succession, following ideas and thoughts only to let go of them in the same breath. It was a brittle sort of excitement, the sort that brings very small children to the point of laughter just as quickly as it brings them to tears. In an effort to hold onto everything I succeeded in holding onto nothing and only began to feel settled when my father said that he thought he heard a car. I welcomed the chance to focus my attention. Very consciously I framed my expression into the most alert shape I could manage and with my head tilted to one side listened to the hackney car tearing down the station road.

Leaving the engine running, the hackney man rushed onto the platform. When he saw us he slapped his forehead and held his expression of surprise until our smiles broke into laughter. The way he said 'Jesus' was in itself welcoming. Every time he went to speak he said it again. Eventually he followed through with a garbled explanation as to why he had not been there to meet the train. He said he couldn't remember ever being late for the afternoon train before. And on the very day we were on it, if only he had known we were going to be on it, Jesus. We listened to everything he had to say, delighted to be listening, hearing only the sound of the words and the rhythm, all the time smiling as though we were listening to music we knew so well that the pleasure of listening to it lay more in anticipating each phrase than actually hearing it. But he was familiar in other ways too. He had taken his place in the stories and incidents that made up my father's world. He had become the greatest of hackney men, the one who had survived, the one who got all the business, because he was the best. But while my father handed out that kind of title to nearly all the people who played a part in the world he had so reluctantly left, the hackney man almost lived up to the description. Down through the years several other people had gone into the same business. They had, for the most part, come home from England. Their cars with yellow registration plates and peculiar registration numbers were usually much plusher than the hackney man's car. Everyone hired them once and then went back to the original hackney man. I think it must have been the way he entered into things. If he was bringing people to a match he would arrive with the car draped in flags and banners. He would begin hooting long before he came into sight and then roar and shout out the window as he approached. When he was bringing people to a dance he leapt out of the car at the collection point and did a sort of rumba. Whatever the event, it started when he arrived. That included funerals. He wept from the moment the mourners got into the car.

He loaded our suitcases into the boot and in a very short time he was talking to us as though we had never been away. He did not ask the question that was to plague us during the week that followed: How long are you home for? instead, he told us about all the Rising celebrations and stopped outside the parochial hall to let us see the big outdoor stage they were building for the occasion. It stretched from the top of the parochial hall steps right out and on to the street. Anyone standing towards the front of the stage would have full command of the square it overlooked. To the right of the hall there was a big marquee. Once he had told us about all the details taken into account when the plans were being made for the celebrations, he started the car again. But then with a sudden violent movement he turned to my father who was sitting in the passenger seat.

'Jesus, you'll be, I forgot, you'll be up there, aren't you supposed to be getting one of the medals.'

We were sitting in the back, smiling, edging forward a little, waiting for him to continue.

He began by listing the feats of my father's generation, saying how magnificent they were, picking his words as if he was addressing a public gathering. Before long we were looking solemnly at those great years when the whole nation was on the march to freedom. Everything around us in the town that afternoon, the stage, the bunting, the marquee and the tricolours that hung from the windows, seemed to point back to a more important era than the world to which I thought we were returning. So, when about ten minutes later we drove up outside our house and I stepped out of the hackney car, I felt caged in that past, unable to break loose, rush headlong and grasp the world I came to reclaim.

I tried to move away from the car and follow Bríd who was walking at a rapid pace towards our gate but I was overcome by the sort of fear that sometimes overcame me when, back in London, I was crossing the High Street down at the intersection. I could not move. All I could do was stand there, watching as she made her way down the path to the door of our house. With each step she grew less familiar until she stood in front of the broken door looking like the film star she had become in England. Her hair waved back from her forehead and caught the light so that everything around her softened and blurred. Even the way she stood, holding one side of her coat collar against her cheek, made her glamorous and the house derelict. I twisted the heel of my Beatle boot into the gravel, turning it with fierce concentration, trying above all else not to cry. In spite of my efforts I lost the battle. But it was not sadness that made me cry. It was nothing as drawn out as that, it felt more like anger. And there was the continuous distraction of scents and smells, leading back to things I had not thought about since we left.

Bríd tried to go into the house but the door would not open. We learned later that it had been boarded up from the inside. She called my father who had gone across to Moratorium Row. He gestured to us to go on up to Queenie's and then, raising his chin and speaking loudly, said he would follow us up later. He stood before two old men who were sitting on the wall. They greeted him in an offhand way as though he had been gone for only a few minutes. Plonked on the wall beside these men were two large bulky objects covered with black plastic and tied in two or three places with yellow baling twine. Behind these objects, which were about the same size as the men themselves, was a low scaffold with two planks thrown roughly on top of it.

Bríd thanked the hackney man for stopping to let us look at the house.

'It'll take a bit of mending, were you thinking of staying there tonight?'

He looked in the rear view mirror, waiting for her to reply.

'In a day or two, perhaps.' She spoke with her public voice, the one she used in England. It was strained and slow, every word deliberate, individually shaped so that she would be clearly understood. Suddenly it seemed false in a theatrical sort of way. I wanted to shake her, shout at her, tell her that we were back home again now and she didn't have to speak like that. But I just listened while she said vague things about being home as if she had a take-it or leave-it attitude to it all. The possibility that she might have changed in a permanent way crossed my mind.

But when we got out of the car at Queenie's she started laughing skittishly—mimicking her own vagueness in the hackney car. She made it clear that she was playing a part not only for the hackney man but for his wife and everyone else he would tell of our arrival. She laughed loudly as she told Queenie, in detail, everything that had happened since we got off the train. She made the smallest of these things appear funny and we laughed, rising and sinking with her, as we had done over the past two and a half years.

Meaisín Ama

(Do Ph. Ó. F.)

MÁIRE MHAC AN TSAOI

An raibh fhios agaibh gur féidir taisteal
Céad bliain abhaile
Le CIE?

Ag Gráinseach Mhóclaeir éireoir agus deir an tiománaí,
'Where are you going to, Missus? You're not there yet.'
'My grandfather's buried beyond,' adéarfad; 'Missus,' le
    colg,
'You can't even tell me the name of this place.'
Éirím as an áiteamh.

Tuirling ag Carraig na Siúire, tá bean romhat adéarfaidh,
'My uncle was Michael Bowers . . . '
Mhúin seisean scríbhneoireacht dom' uncail-se;
Bé cainteoir deireannach dúchais é i Muileann na gCloch . . .
'We're not exactly related: my great-aunt stood for your mother.
You'll be going to Nine Mile House?'

Ní cathair mar a tuairisc í an Charraig;
Cár ghabh an ghalántacht mhór?
'Not made; it was bought in Carrick . . .'
'Carrick and the black sky over it!'
Agus báisteach ag tórmach ó dheas,
'And sweet Kilcash . . .'

Is cuimhin liom an Charraig lá aonaigh:
Dob'fhaill treacha iad ciosaí na sráide;
Ba ghleanntán doimhin í an tsráid;
Agus toise os chionn nádúire
Do bhíodh i mbeithígh agus daoine.
Leibhéal na sráide ardaithe ó shoin—
'Carrick, I dread you!'

Time Machine

(For P. O F.)

MÁIRE MHAC AN TSAOI

Did you know it was possible to travel
A hundred years home
With CIE?

At Grangemockler you will stand up and the driver says,
'Where are you going to, Missus? You're not there yet.'
'My grandfather's buried beyond,' I will say; 'Missus,'
with enmity,
'You can't even tell me the name of this place.'
I abandon contention.

Get down at Carrick-on-Suir, a woman waiting will say,
'My uncle was Michael Bowers . . . '
He taught *my* uncle to write;
He was the last native speaker of Irish in Mulnagloch . . .
'We're not exactly related: my great-aunt stood for your mother.
You'll be going to Nine Mile House?'

Carrick does not live up to its fame;
Where has the grandeur gone?
'Not made; it was bought in Carrick . . .'
'Carrick and the black sky over it!'
And rain threatening to the south,
'And sweet Kilcash . . .'

I remember Carrick on a fair day:
The kerbs of the street were cliffs;
The street was a deep ravine;
And people and cattle
Were more than natural size.
The street-level has risen since—
'Carrick, I dread you!'

Teach na Naoi Míle 's an fháilte chinéalta ó Mhary 's a céile—
A dó 's a dó iad clann na beirte deirféar: í féin is mo
mháthair.
Is cuimhin léi mise im' bunóic, agus scríonn sí bhéarsaí
filíochta;
Do bhíodh ana-lámh aici, cloisim, ar chuite 'oiliúint
chun cursála . . .

Mac a deirféar-san, Dick Tobin, thug ag triall mé ar
fhearann na nGearaltach:
Baile Uí Dhúgáin sa Ghaolainn? Balladuggan againn-ne á
thabhairt air.
Ansan, ar an seanabhaile, bhí tiarnas ag 'Boss' Fitzgerald;
Is ann a bhunaíodar thar nais taréis dóibh a gcur as a
seilbh.

An t-achar san ar thaobh an bhóthair, 'dhaineanaigh meon
na muintire;
B'shin droim scartha gach uisce:
Cúl le dealús faoi nearr
Mise stroinséartha sa láthair.

Fuar agus dorcha an tigh . . .
Agus beag; cár thoilleadar uile?
Cuid acu anois san Astráil;
Fáisceann an duairceas faoim' croí . . .
'First cousins, once removed, cannot be replaced!'

'Abhaile linn tré Chill Chais,' adeir Dick, 'Buaileam
bóthar';
Ní maith leis an caomhnú nua atá acu ar an séipéal ann.
Cloistear cling tua le crann fós anso t'réis na mblianta;
Is lasaimse le teann náire:
Mo chéad chuaird riamh ar an bhfód so!
Anóthair, na cianta cé, nach lá iad 'Na radharc-san?

'An fada go Bail' Áth' Cliath?'
Dúch é an freagra, 'Is fada.'

Nine Mile House and the kindly welcome of Mary and of
    her husband—
The second degree of kin are two sisters' children: herself
    and my mother.
She remembers me as a baby and she writes verses of
    poetry;
I am told she was a great hand at rearing grey-hounds for
    coursing . . .

Her sister's son, Dick Tobin, brought me to see the old
    Fitzgerald homestead:
Baile Uí Dhúgáin in Irish? We knew it as Balladuggan.
The old house was the lordship of 'Boss' Fitzgerald;
It was there the family resettled after they were evicted.

That stint on the side of the road hardened their
    disposition;
That water-shed split all waters:
Rejection of destitution
Made me a stranger here.

The house is cold and dark . . .
And small; where did they all fit?
Some of them now in Australia;
Desolation squeezes my heart . . .
'First cousins, once removed, cannot be replaced!'

'Let's go home by Kilcash,' says Dick, 'Hit the road';
He doesn't like the new conservation bit in the chapel
The sound of the axe to the tree is still heard down the
years here;
And I glow with shame to think:
My first ever visit!
And yet, are uncounted ages not as a day in His sight? . . .

'Is it far then to Dublin?'
The answer is gloomy, 'It's far.'

Home

PAULA MEEHAN

I am the blind woman finding her way home by a map of
tune.
When the song that is in me is the song I hear from the
world
I'll be home. It's not written down and I don't remember
the words.
I know when I hear it I'll have made it myself. I'll be
home.

A version I heard once in Leitrim was close, a wet Tuesday
night
in the Sean Relig bar. I had come for the session, I stayed
for the vision and lore. The landlord called time,
the music dried up, the grace notes were pitched to the
dark.
When the jukebox blared out *I'd only four senses and he left
me senseless*,
I'd no choice but to take to the road. On Grafton Street
in November
I heard a mighty sound: a travelling man with a didgeridoo
blew me clear to Botany Bay. The tune too far back to live in
but scribed on my bones. In a past life I may have been
Kangaroo,
rocked in my dreamtime, convict ships coming o'er the
foam.

In the Puzzle Factory one winter I was sure I was home.
The talking in tongues, the riddles, the rhymes, struck a
chord
that cut through the pharmaceutical haze. My rhythm
catatonic,
I lulled myself back to the womb, my mother's heart

beating the drum of herself and her world. I was tricked
by her undersong, just close enough to my own. I took then
to dancing; I spun like a Dervish. I swear I heard the subtle
music of the spheres. It's no place to live, but—
out there in space, on your own hung, aloft the night.
The tune was in truth a mechanical drone;
I was a pitiful monkey jigging on cue. I came back to
      earth
with a land, to rain on my face, to sun in my hair. And
      grateful too.

The wisewomen say you must live in your skin, call *it*
      home,
no matter how battered or broken, misused by the world,
      you can heal.
This morning a letter arrived on the nine o'clock post.
The Department of Historical Reparation, and who did I
      blame?
The Nuns? Your Mother? The State? *Tick box provided,*
we'll consider your case. I'm burning my soapbox, I'm
      taking
the very next train. A citizen of nowhere, nothing to my
      name.

I'm on my last journey. Though my lines are all wonky
they spell me a map that makes sense. Where the song
      that is in me
is the song I hear from the world, I'll set down my burdens
and sleep. The spot that I lie on at last the place I'll call
      home.

Home

PATRICK MCCABE

A tiny sliver of firelight glinted in the cat's eyes as Annie paused above the range, gaunt and black as the poker she held, grey threads of hair tucked beneath the limp beret. The lace curtain wavered as the knock came again, two gentle taps, her eyes narrowed as she strove to name its touch. A shaft of sunlight threw a tilted square on the floor, a weakening bluebottle clacked in a corner of the window. He stood in the doorway, her tongue smoothed a bulge in her cheek as she surveyed the plaid suit and thin moustache, the belted suitcases at his knee.

'Well,' he said, 'I'm—'

'Home,' she interjected as she wiped her hands on the black skirt, her head jerking towards the kitchen.

'Long journey,' he said, 'hold-up at Liverpool, thought I'd never . . .'

He broke off and stared wide-eyed at me.

'Not Benny's lad?'

She answered with her eyes amid the clanging of pans.

'Bloody hell,' he said, grasping my hand, 'last time you were that size. Tell me, is he well, your dad?'

'He's ok,' I replied, 'the best . . .'

'Still the same,' she said from the kitchen, 'never comes near me from the day he married, that's the thanks you get.'

He squeezed my arm, then rose and drummed on his lapels as he stared out across the fairgreen, colourful bodies languishing beside a transistor, 'Hey Jude, don't make it bad . . .'

'I saw The Beatles once,' he said, 'not far from where I work, crossing the road would you believe . . .'

'You're doing well,' she called, 'I got your card at Christmas . . . and the other . . .'

'Oh just a few shillings Annie, Ellen's got a bit put by, we're not so bad . . .'

'What were they like?' I quizzed.

'Just like lads really. Lennon, he's the mad one. Got it up here though I daresay.'

He tapped his temple.

I thought of cut stone squares and red kiosks, Lennon with a guitar and white suit, the sun shining on his round spectacles.

'England is the best,' I said.

He rummaged in the suitcase, the postcard he held up split in four, a Beefeater at a portcullis, Piccadilly neon flashing SKOL.

'The city of cities,' he smiled, 'it never sleeps.'

'How is she?' asked Annie, 'is she . . .?'

He hesitated, his brow tightened as he replied:

'She . . . she isn't well by times . . .'

She set the meal on the table and sucked in her wrinkled cheeks. Her eyes flitted as she made a cage of her fingers.

'We all have our crosses to bear,' she said, edging into the grey interior of the scullery.

We sat on the summer seat listening to the Smithboro Fife and Drum Band playing 'Yellow Submarine'. Mothers lay back with sweaters knotted about their necks, children were mesmerised by the huge bass drum. He dressed like nobody from the town, his shoes shone and his short-sleeved shirt was starched rigid.

'Tell me more,' I said.

'Oh it were a strange place at first, lad, I'll tell you no word of a lie. I wasn't much older than you when I stood in Euston Station for t' first time, put the fear of God in me it did. Spent the bloody night in the YMCA Hall. Kept my money well hidden in my boots there, lad. Bloke next to me kept staring over at me the whole night long—never took his eyes off me. But you live and you learn, lad, got me first job in a post office went from there to a hundred different jobs, wound up with near two hundred pound a week. Were well worth it, lad.'

'How come you and da lived with Annie years ago?' I asked.

He looked at me in a funny kind of way. Then he stood up and said:

'Here, come on lad, let's go for a drink.'

As soon as the barman saw the way he was dressed, he rushed over and served him straight away.

'Nice pub this,' he said, 'when I left it were falling down, the windows bricked up . . .'

The lager shone golden in his hand as his eyes scanned the bar.

'Cheers,' he said to a customer bent over the counter, 'time doesn't be long passing . . .'

'You're not from about here,' said the customer, closing one eye and dragging on his cigarette.

'Well, I was,' he replied, 'England now.'

The customer sucked his teeth and tapped the cigarette.

'Aye, ye sound England,' he said, then lapsed into silence.

He sipped his lager and said:

'You could come over on a holiday. I'd take you to see United on a Saturday.'

The Old Trafford cheer rose in my head, George Best's raven black hair flapped as he emerged waving from the tunnel.

'Busby's Babes. They drink in my local, The Green Man. Every Friday night—you could see them when you come over. The Red Devils.'

He raised his glass and smiled. The other customer stumbled as he was leaving. He took his arm and helped him up. The customer stared into his face.

'If you're so fond of England,' he said, 'why the hell don't you stay there?'

He kept staring as if he was going to say something else but then he just tossed his cigarette impatiently to the floor and left.

We stayed there for a long time after that. He kept saying we would leave soon but we didn't. Then he leaned over to me and asked me to go down for da.

'Your dad and me's half-brothers, lad. We came up together. Annie took us from the home—the nuns . . .'

I didn't know what he meant, he kept hesitating between sentences.

'You'll go down?'

'Yes,' I said.

When da came into the pub, they shook hands. They started talking about the old days. As he spoke, his voice got louder, da kept looking around him to see who was listening.

'Times were bad then, eh Benny,' he said. 'Like a ghost town, this place was, bloody Dev and bloody disease . . .'

'Aye. Times were tough,' said da under his breath.

'Soon as this lad's old enough, send him over to me, I'll fix him up. Fifty pound a week start, ok lad? Nothing for you here.'

Then he started talking about the home in Belfast. Da didn't really want to talk about it at all, he kept shifting in his seat and swirling the stout in his glass.

'The only one who ever gave us anything was Sister Stanislaus. She was the only one who had any heart.'

He kept on about it, the blazer they wore there, the gravelled quadrangle, the smell of the waxed corridors.

Once, when my mother had asked da about the home, a dark, hunted sort of expression came over his face. The more he listened now, the more his face became like that. Then suddenly he slapped the counter with his hand and cried:

'That's enough about it! Jesus, every year you bring it up! That's enough about the cursed place!'

The cigarette trembled in da's fingers as they sat there in silence with the barman staring out at them from the shadows beneath the television.

My mother kissed him on the cheek when she came in. They opened bottles and began to drink again. His shirt was crumpled now and there was money sticking out of his back pocket. He stretched and said to my mother:

'You see this little lad here? Best lad going. Come next summer, I'm going to show him the sights. Old Trafford, the lot. He can stay with me and Ellen.'

He drank a toast to that and kept talking about how great England was and how good it had been to him, then said:

'And it'll be good to you when you come over.'

Then da set his drink down on the table and said in a slow,

deliberate voice:

'He's going no place.'

His face was white. My mother tried to dissuade him with her eyes.

'England,' he said, then drew a deep breath. He looked at me. 'Did he tell you about Ellen? Well?'

I didn't answer. I looked from one to the other.

'Did he tell you he's married to a woman twice his age? Half-blind and hates him from the day she married him?'

I could see the glass shaking in his hand as da spoke.

'Married an auld woman because he was afraid to ask anyone else. Closing a gate in a backstreet factory this twenty years. Wears a wee blue suit with brass buttons and tips his cap to his betters. Aye, England, he says, same charade every year.'

A terrible silence came into the room.

'Benny,' he began, but the words did not come out. He rose unsteadily, then turned and awkwardly opened the door, feeling his way along the dark hallway. Da just sat there in silence taking an odd sharp gulp from his whiskey glass. My mother fixed him with a biting stare, I had never seen her look at him like that.

'You never got over the home either, did you? *Did you?*' she said.

Then she got up and left the room, I could see she was about to cry.

Into the small hours I thought of him, on a high stool in The Green Man beneath the framed photographs of Manchester United, staring into the trademarked mirror where an officious, younger Annie, far away from the stifling smoke and frenzied conversation, stood at the end of a waxed corridor, waiting patiently for their footsteps to approach along the stark, echoing tiles.

Epiphyte

AISLING MAGUIRE

The Portrait

' . . . and this is Adelaide, daughter of the house. She was found dead in a hotel bedroom, age thirty.' The guide twitches the bodice of her Southern belle gown. 'Of course there were lots of stories.'

I'll bet. That's not the face of an elopee. Adelaide was lighting out. Hotel bedrooms do a body in after a while. I know them, inch for anonymous inch. She is tossed on the bed like an empty. Ah me.

I live on air, don't know when my feet last touched the earth, flit in cabs from airports to burnished towers that sway in the wind. Stepping between the cab and the revolving door I feel that I have shucked a husk to stand naked on the sidewalk. Ready to be mugged.

Maybe that was how she died, lonely girl, a prowler through the window, knife at her throat, clash of groins, flurry of blood linen stifled cries. Absolute silence. Her few jewels and dollars gone. Alas.

Home Sweet Home

What did she flee? That father too like her, his painted profile still watching hers. A home that the guide likes to tell us 'shows the power of money, folks.' Soirées, ghostly white oaks, sugar cane, stifling heat, sorrow of the slaves, reek of the bayou. 'Bye bye' she cried. 'I'll go to the city, find my fortune.'

Oh babe, how were you to know the knife was being sharpened?

See me: that hybrid creature, Career Woman; careering through the corporate world in my shoulder pads, underwired bra, lycra tights, briefcase. Barbie by another name. Those bankers judge my body not my word. The power of inches. Grotesque fumbling over cocktails and one night stands that deepen the loneliness. It's a sham. No one believes in it. We do it with mirrors.

My tipple is 'home sweet home': a shot of whiskey and a line of coke. No ice. No water. No pain.

The Wall

The guide moves us along. (This is a board game: hopping from square to square picking up trivia—but where is home?)

What's this? A room that's not a room. Not demolished but undressed, to show how the building was put together. The ceiling is shorn to expose timber ribs. Stripped of plaster the wall appears in cross-section: Spanish moss, the grey beard that festoons the trees hereabouts (useful also as an explosive), packed in over a pudding of oyster shells and bayou mud.

The house has roots; has triumphed over the slime which I feel now oozing between my toes. My head spins. Those shells echo with fiddles and washboards, and the argot of families strung together by variants of a single name—Jeanne, Jeanine, Jeanette, Jeanne-Marie, permutations on a pair of genes imported from the old world—eating alligator flesh, tasting the chemical soup, arcadia backsliding into the mud. As soon this house, no longer home. We build like the spider now, skywriters.

Adelaide smelt the rot in the wall.

The Bishop's Bedroom

I'm on the lam here, mingling with the corporate wives. Or spouses/significant others? The lingo has outstripped me. Some of the older men have come too. They've heard the hype and the figures before. What do they care, counting their days? I should be listening to a pitch on the family of brands. My brothers and sisters in the Lie. The power of numbers.

Instead here I am admiring the bishop's bed. A marvellous toy. Fantastical steeples of polished wood ascend at its corners, spheres spindles pears tears, interlocking and detachable. The prelate could take up his bed and travel.

I catch the deepthroated curses of the slaves as they toss the wooden orbs back and forth wondering which of them the holy visitor would importune, unless he chose their mistress, Adelaide's mother?

One thing's for sure, no ascetic ever lay in that bed.

My old Granda went monastic after my parents died (Da struck by a coronary as he tied his shoelace; Ma a year later of grief, they say). The day I buried my dolls he frightened me, his voice intoning above my head.

'I always wanted to live in a birch forest,' he said.

I glanced up but he was staring into the bushes, seeing his skeletal trees slice the darkness, savouring the silence lodged between them. I was so spooked I exhumed the dolls, carried them indoors, bathed them, put them to bed and cried. For my cruelty to them? For myself crossing the shadowy frontier between child and adult? For the old man's fix on death?

Napoleon's Bath

Now we are in the bathroom, large enough to sleep a family of five. At its centre stands a marble tub, a faultline, the work of vandals, dividing the pure stone. Like this house the bath has been salvaged to return us to our past.

The story goes that Napoleon sent it to Adelaide's great grandmother after her honeymoon audience in his court.

The guide smirks, 'They thought baths were a great invention in Europe back then.'

I feel the group's eyes slide over me, doubting my advance on the nineteenth century.

Perhaps, captivated by the Louisiana bride—child of his civilisation adrift in a barbaric world he had yet to conquer—the Emperor dreamt her, pale as the egret, making her beauty monumental in this bath, remembering him.

I picture her hooting with laughter at the man's folly, refusing to sit in the trough until years later she allowed her children to splash there like birds in a puddle, then lulled them with tales of the little corporal's apotheosis and exile.

In Paris worshippers are weeping over his tomb while here we praise the power shower, calculate the stress on the floorboards, sneakingly regret the loss of time to wallow.

I dislike what I see in the merciless light of hotel bathrooms, mocked in some mirrors by the prima donna's frame of bulbs exposing the scars of narrow escapes and mistakes. How many times can the body be invaded, pillaged and shut? How many times did the knife cut that girl? How long did she lie, her organs and blood struggling to continue their task while life slipped away? Did the shock rend her family, unbalancing their life?

Down here the ground, reclaimed from the swamp, is so soft that bodies must be housed above it lest they surface and roam in a rainstorm. The graveyards are miniature cities, their marble avenues stalked by pickpockets and rapists. No sanctuary there.

The Garconnière

Here Adelaide's brother would have slept, the boys traditionally set apart at puberty, the room an annexe, permitting him to leave and sow his wild oats unhindered and unobserved. The blind eye. Down in the shacks beside the sugar cane, the slave girls lay, invisible. In town the quadroons emerged from leafy courtyards to sit on balconies where moonlight netted their sultry skin in wrought iron shadows and they dreamt of a home and family life of their own. A little further off in darkness' outer circle voodoo dancers bit off chickens' heads and, as the wings continued to beat, took the insistent blood between their legs and flew to their ancestors.

Night was crammed with noise and touch.

While I lay awake, eyes hugging the crack of light in the doorway, I heard my parents' voices next door. Close as a mother's heartbeat to an infant, it was the sound of love which lingers like a tune half-remembered, never to be retrieved.

Adelaide's brother stands in the morgue shaking his head and saying 'No this is not my sister.' The figure before him is a stranger. She could be anyone's sister lover wife daughter. She is not the girl he recalls kicking under the table, leading by the hand through the sugar cane to see the hidden still, dressing up as a man to ride on a night's adventure into town. She is nobody but he can't turn away from her. He knows as he leaves that cold room he will spend the rest of his days searching for his sister while the body he has seen tagged with her name will disintegrate in the stone house where his ancestors are interred.

The Whistling Gallery

With each return to the old sod I feel less at home. My heart recoils when the jet peels off the runway at JFK and I tell myself this is the last visit. I have done all the weddings and funerals. There is nothing more to go back to. And every year again I am strapped into that seat, my own fault, hearing the cúpla focail and waking to a view of sodden fields and a dose of the *Indo*.

It's not the puny glass and steel cubes or the multi-lane highways that rattle me with their aspiration toward the confidence of the place I now call home. It's more a confusion of identity. When I walk down the familiar streets I am nudged by the echo of the person I would have been had I stayed. That person, and her children, no doubt.

And, fatally, recently, the impulse has taken me to hire a car and hightail it out of the city. So far I have resisted, knowing that if I cross the Shannon I am lost. No map. No compass. Watch stopped and not a Visa sign in sight. There's no denying the power of that abiding water stone heather silence, a sediment in my blood. I must be getting old. Like Granda.

Back here in the labyrinth being a stranger feels right. No flight of time; the school chum who rapidly calculates the price of your clothes; the ex-boyfriend thickening with complacency. No sirree. Here you just tip the wing and fly past.

The smell of cooking has long evaporated from this kitchen. Now all is scoured and sanitised save for the circular mat of woven corn shucks roped off at the centre of the flagged floor. Stained by time it is the colour of dried blood. My fingers itch to touch the mesh of fibres but it defies me with the taboo that rings a bird's nest.

As the guide conjures the heat of this room when the ovens were stoked and summer's humidity seeped in, my breathing stalls.

This blockage tightens as we walk through the whistling gallery, a narrow corridor linking kitchen to dining room, where serving boys were compelled to whistle and so reassure the master that they were not picking at the food they carried.

Absurdly, I think of canaries in the mines.

Home

We return to the hall (often flooded but deemed a ballroom nevertheless) where the guide, twirling on her Nikes—no Scarlett she—flounces her skirt to demonstrate how the ladies checked their hems for slippage in the mirror set below the bureau. From a daybed in the corner nursing mothers could watch the dance, and in an adjoining room children could 'fais do do'. No one was permitted to miss the fun.

Poor Adelaide stands in a corner, cheeks hectic after a glass of punch, eyes dulled by the spectacle of her life circling before her while her pulse quickens to the chant of escape, a note she has caught from the whistling gallery. She smells the damp of recent flooding, her world corrupting.

I shake my head at the ghost. I too thought I could run from pain, reinvent my life, cheat death. We were wrong Addie. I am drowning up here in the air. I must descend, put down roots.

Our voices fall heavily in this room. The history trip is over. We are being evicted. Outside I shiver in the heat and throw a few aerobics shapes. I am ready to walk.

The Town He Had Hated Most

SEBASTIAN BARRY

Having been a largely extra citizen of Ireland, Africa, Europe and America, Moran went back to Sligo with fifty pounds and an unshakeable wish to be left alone. He didn't have to work too hard to achieve this.

He was sixty when he walked into the town he had hated most in the world, and he was a curiosity that the townspeople had to relearn. The bishop was long dead, and no one seemed to recognize him. Certainly anyone who had known him as the Blessed Apostle was either perished or gone away.

He took possession of a disused bridge carrying a grassed-over road that had been superseded by a larger one on another route. The bridge had only spanned a dry gully, and he made a house out of one side of that, under the arch. A policeman came out to talk to him once or twice, but Moran was so silent and simple that he was, as he desired, left to himself.

He was obviously not an idiot because he could do his shopping as well as the next man, and the countryside was well-stocked with bachelors who cycled into town on a Wednesday, without uttering more than ten words to the shopkeepers. Moran had only his legs, but he carried a linoleum bag like the rest of them. Here he put cabbages and potatoes and bacon and dripping, as it was handed over the scrubbed counters to him.

The children of his dead tormentors treated him as was his due, a poor single man living on his army pension in the best habitation he could muster. He suspected the town had changed, and it was as good as if he had never been there before. It was possibly the one place on the globe he could be truly unknown—he believed in the principle that lightning never strikes twice on the one tree.

He had nothing to look forward to, so he made a virtue of each day, or did his best at it. Often, though he was old, he was not lonely, and as he suspected the summers were the easiest season. He had always had a taste for a bit of sun and wild animals and grass, and he enjoyed these things like books. Every week that he got through with a measure of peace made him stronger for the next. He was completely without virtue perhaps, but on the other hand he lacked significant vices. Perhaps Moran had no true ability to love other people, but he didn't love himself either. Apart from a longing for women, which he didn't feel anymore, he had never aspired much to the companionship of other travellers, or if he had, he had met with such little success that he began to think a thing like that was impossible. Most men were more powerful than he was, and there didn't seem to be any area in the departments of life in which he excelled or even glimmered, so the neatest thing for him to do was retreat, and retreat he did.

In winter he felt like winter, and he always expected to be dead before the end of it. To be dead was a sort of solid respectable phrase which he never bothered to entertain himself with. Since he had nothing to give up and no one to leave, he couldn't really imagine it, so he left it alone. This was a bit irritating for me, but I endured it for his sake.

He spent a great deal of his mornings talking to a woman he called Moll, and I often used to pretend that I was she. This shouldn't be seen as a sign of weakness on my part, but actually a type of generosity. I found it light enough to assume the character of a patient interested woman, and as he never knew anything about it, it hurt no one.

I have always taken a superior attitude to Moran since this was appropriate, and it would have been ridiculous to pretend ever that he had much to recommend him, besides his affectionate ignorance. But still I know I was well fond of him, and he was harmless enough in himself for me to be a bit agitated when the weather was very bad, or he seemed unhappy. He had a way of being unhappy without being foolish that was perhaps quite rare. Of course he was foolish in everything else, and he wasn't often unhappy as I say. Still, he had a few good qualities.

I feel apologetic for him—or rather for myself, in that I was so long with him—because he appeared so trampish and was so unsought-after by other people. Of course I had to stay with him, but that was a grotesque combination at best. It's not very encouraging to like someone whom no one else even takes the trouble to dislike. This wasn't so in his youth and middle years, and in those rather arbitrary years it might have been possible for him to rise above his abysmal stature or perhaps be elevated by some pleasant accident. But he was a bit of a Jonah in his own boat, and I minded that from time to time. He didn't seem to care at all. And now that he was over sixty and beyond meddling with, there was really no one but myself to notice it.

The catalogue of his pleasures was childish—tall grass, shades of grass, good level-headed sunshine, a clean river, shades of water of this, river birds, grass birds, night birds, especially the owl. He had a preference for owls that he never lost, even into his last day. He liked them because no one ever saw them, or rarely, and only when the owls chose it. He liked them because the owl had a steady informative call. It was so regular he sometimes wondered as he listened to it whether it was real at all, or just some important part of the general soil, a natural clock for the likes of himself. He thought of owls in the plural sometimes although he only ever heard one, but he heard it for so many years, in so many places, that he could calculate there would have to be more than one such engine. Unless owls were similar to the moon, in that the moon was singular but lived everywhere. He supposed there had to be more than the one—all the same he hoped the owl was like the moon, and called over the world, but was still alone. He would believe it if anyone ever told him about some plurality of owls, but until he was told he preferred to think of just the one, when he could.

The best nights indeed were the ones when the sky was open, and the moon got in, and filled everywhere with its light, and the owl thrummed in its machinery. That simple note plumbed Moran, and represented far more comprehensively than a book all the oddments and jumps of his life. It was comprehensive, but at the same time trimmed and compact, and he could almost think of his life, as he listened to the owl, as something that he could hold in his own hand. He could lie back, under the bridge, behind the lengths of wood, and the moon could come in there, and he could hold everything like a toy.

That's what made me fond of him really. But he got away from me, slipped away, in some way free of everything, in a better way free of me. And he heard in his heart the mysterious perfect heart of the owl.

What a Surprise the Familiar Is

JOHN BANVILLE

It was early afternoon when I reached Coolgrange. I got down at the cross and watched the bus lumber away, its fat back-end looking somehow derisive. The noise of the engine faded, and the throbbing silence of summer settled again on the fields. The sky was still overcast, but the sun was asserting itself somewhere, and the light that had been dull and flat was now a tender, pearl-grey glow. I stood and looked about me. What a surprise the familiar always is. It was all there, the broken gate, the drive, the long meadow, the oak wood—home!—all perfectly in place, waiting for me, a little smaller than I remembered, like a scale-model of itself. I laughed. It was not really a laugh, more an exclamation of startlement and recognition. Before such scenes as this—trees, the shimmering fields, that mild soft light—I always feel like a traveller on the point of departure. Even arriving I seemed to be turning away, with a lingering glance at the lost land. I set off up the drive with my raincoat over my shoulder and my battered bag in my hand, a walking cliché, though it's true I was a bit long in the tooth, and a bit on the beefy side, for the part of the prodigal son. A dog slid out of the hedge at me with a guttural snarl, teeth bared to the gums. I halted. I do not like dogs. This was a black-and-white thing with shifty eyes, it moved back and forth in a half-circle in front of me, still growling, keeping its belly close to the ground. I held the suitcase against my knees for a shield, and spoke sharply, as to an unruly child, but my voice came out a broken falsetto, and for a moment there was a sense of general merriment, as if there were faces hidden among the leaves, laughing. Then a whistle sounded, and the brute whined and turned guiltily toward the house. My mother was standing on the front steps. She laughed. Suddenly the sun came out, with a kind of soundless report. Good God, she said, it is you, I thought I was seeing things.

I hesitate. It is not that I am lost for words, but the opposite. There is so much to be said that I do not know where to begin. I feel myself staggering backwards slowly, clutching in my outstretched arms a huge, unwieldy and yet weightless burden. She is so much, and, at the same time, nothing. I must go carefully, this is perilous ground. Of course, I know that whatever I say will be smirked at knowingly by the amateur psychologists packing the court. When it comes to the subject of mothers, simplicity is not permitted. All the same, I shall try to be honest and clear. Her name is Dorothy, though everyone has always called her Dolly, I do not know why, for there is nothing doll-like about her. She is a large, vigorous woman with the broad face and heavy hair of a tinker's wife. In describing her thus I do not mean to be disrespectful. She is impressive, in her way, at once majestic and slovenly. I recall her from my childhood as a constant but remote presence, statuesque, blank-eyed, impossibly handsome in an Ancient Roman sort of way, like a marble figure at the far side of a lawn. Later on, though, she grew to be top-heavy, with a big backside and slim legs, a contrast which, when I was an adolescent and morbidly interested in such things, led me to speculate on the complicated architecture that must be necessary to bridge the gap under her skirt between those shapely knees and that thick waist. Hello, mother, I said, and looked away from her, casting about me crossly for something neutral on which to concentrate. I was annoyed already. She has that effect on me. I have only to stand before her and instantly the irritation and resentment begin to seethe in my breast. I was surprised. I had thought that after ten years there would be at least a moment of grace between our meeting and the first attack of filial heartburn, but not a bit of it, here I was, jaw clenched, glaring venomously at a tuft of weed sprouting from a crack in the stone steps where she stood. She was not much changed. Her bosom, which cries out to be called ample, had descended to just above her midriff. Also she had grown a little moustache. She wore baggy corduroy trousers and a cardigan with sagging pockets. She came down the steps to me and laughed again. You have put on weight, Freddie, she said, you've got fat.

212

Then she reached out and—this is true, I swear it—and took hold of a piece of my stomach and rolled it playfully between a finger and thumb. This woman, this woman—what can I say? I was thirty-eight, a man of parts, with a wife and a son and an impressive Mediterranean tan, I carried myself with gravitas and a certain faint air of menace, and she, what did she do?—she pinched my belly and laughed her phlegmy laugh. Is it any wonder I have ended up in jail? Is it? The dog, seeing that I was to be accepted, sidled up to me and tried to lick my hand, which gave me an opportunity to deliver it a good hard kick in the ribs. That made me feel better, but not much, and not for long.

Is there anything as powerfully, as piercingly evocative, as the smell of the house in which one's childhood was spent? I try to avoid generalisations, as no doubt the court has noticed, but surely this is a universal, this involuntary spasm of recognition which comes with the first whiff of that humble, drab, brownish smell, which is hardly a smell at all, more an emanation, a sort of sigh exhaled by the thousands of known but unacknowledged tiny things that collectively constitute what is called home. I stepped into the hall and for an instant it was as if I had stepped soundlessly through the membrane of time itself. I faltered, tottering inwardly. Hatstand with broken umbrella, that floor tile, still loose. Get out, Patch, damn you! my mother said behind me, and the dog yelped. The taste of apples unaccountably flooded my mouth. I felt vaguely as if something momentous had happened, as if in the blink of an eye everything around me had been whipped away and replaced instantly with an exact replica, perfect in every detail, down to the last dust-mote. I walked on, into this substitute world, tactfully keeping a blank expression, and seemed to hear a disembodied held breath being let go in relief that the difficult trick had worked yet again.

We went into the kitchen. It looked like the lair of some large, scavenging creature. Lord, mother, I said, are you living here? Items of clothing, an old woman's nameless rags, were stuffed between the dishes on the dresser. The toes of three or four pairs of shoes peeped out from under a cupboard, an unnerving sight, as if the wearers might be huddled together in there, stubby arms clasped around each other's hunched shoulders, listening. Pieces of furniture had migrated here from all over the house, the narrow little bureau from my father's study, the walnut cocktail cabinet from the drawing-room, the velvet-covered recliner with balding armrests in which my Great-Aunt Alice, a tiny, terrible woman, had died without a murmur one Sunday afternoon in summer. The huge old wireless that used to lord it over the lounge stood now at a drunken tilt on the draining-board, crooning softly to itself, its single green eye pulsing. The place was far from clean. A ledger was open on the table, and bills and things were strewn amid the smeared plates and the unwashed teacups. She had been doing the accounts. Briefly I considered bringing up the main matter straight away—money, that is— but thought better of it. As if she had an inkling of what was in my mind she glanced from me to the papers and back again with amusement. I turned away from her, to the window. Out on the lawn a stocky girl in jodhpurs was leading a string of Connemara ponies in a circle. I recalled dimly my mother telling me, in one of her infrequent and barely literate letters, about some hare-brained venture involving these animals. She came and stood beside me. We watched in silence the ponies plodding round and round. Ugly brutes, aren't they, she said cheerfully. The simmering annoyance I had felt since arriving was added to now by a sense of general futility. I have always been prone to accidie. It is a state, or, I might even say, a force, the significance of which in human affairs historians and suchlike seem not to appreciate. I think I would do anything to avoid it—anything. My mother was talking about her customers, mostly Japs and Germans, it seemed—They're taking over the bloody country, Freddie, I'm telling you. They bought the ponies as pets for their spoilt offspring, at what she happily admitted were outrageous prices. Cracked, the lot of them, she said. We laughed, and then fell vacantly silent again. The sun was on the lawn, and a vast white cloud was slowly unfurling above the sweltering beeches. I was thinking how strange it was to stand here glooming out at the day like this, bored and irritable, my hands in my pockets, while all the time, deep inside me somewhere, hardly acknowledged, grief dripped and dripped, a kind of silvery ichor, pure, and strangely precious. Home, yes, home is always a surprise.

She insisted that I come and look the place over, as she put it. After all, my boy, she said, someday all this will be yours. And she did her throaty cackle. I did not remember her being so easily amused in the past. There was something almost unruly in her laughter, a sort of abandon. I was a little put out by it, I thought it was not seemly. She lit up a cigarette and set off around the house, with the cigarette box and matches clutched in her left claw, and me trailing grimly in her smoking wake. The house was rotting, in places so badly, and so rapidly, that even she was startled. She talked and talked. I nodded dully, gazing at damp walls and sagging floors and mouldering window-frames. In my old room the bed was broken, and there was something growing in the middle of the mattress. The view from the window—trees, a bit of sloping field, the red roof of a barn— was exact and familiar as an hallucination. Here was the cupboard I had built, and at once I had a vision of myself, a small boy with a fierce frown, blunt saw in hand, hacking at a sheet of plywood, and my grieving heart wobbled, as if it were not myself I was remembering, but something like a son, dear and vulnerable, lost to me forever in the depths of my own past. When I turned around my mother was not there. I found her on the stairs, looking a little odd around the eyes. She set off again. I must see the grounds, she cried, the stables, the oak wood. She was determined I would see everything, everything.

Out of doors my spirits rose somewhat. How soft the air of summer here. I had been too long under harsh southern skies. And the trees, the great trees! those patient, quietly suffering creatures, standing stock-still as if in embarrassment, their tragic gazes somehow turned away from us. Patch the dog—I can see I am going to be stuck with this brute—Patch the dog appeared, rolling its mad eyes and squirming. It followed silently behind us across the lawn. The stable-girl, watching sidelong as we approached, seemed on the point of taking to her heels in fright.

Her name was Joan, or Jean, something like that. Big bum, big chest—obviously mother had felt an affinity. When I spoke to her the poor girl turned crimson, and wincingly extended a calloused little paw as if she were afraid I might be going to keep it. I gave her one of my special, slow smiles, and saw myself through her eyes, a tall, tanned hunk in a linen suit, leaning over her on a summer lawn and murmuring dark words. Tinker! she yelped, get off! The lead pony, a stunted beast with a truculent eye, was edging sideways in that dully determined way that they have, nudging heavily against me. I put my hand on its flank to push it away, and was startled by the solidity, the actuality of the animal, the coarse dry coat, the dense unyielding flesh beneath, the blood warmth. Shocked, I took my hand away quickly and stepped back. Suddenly I had a vivid, queasy sense of myself, not the tanned pin-up now, but something else, something pallid and slack and soft. I was aware of my toenails, my anus, my damp restricted crotch. And I was ashamed. I can't explain it. That is, I could, but won't. Then the dog began to bark, rushing to the pony's hoofs, and the pony snorted, peeling back its muzzle and snapping its alarming teeth. My mother kicked the dog, and the girl hauled the pony's head sideways. The dog howled, the line of ponies plunged and whinnied. What a racket! Everything, always, turns to farce. I remembered my hangover. I needed a drink.

INDEX OF AUTHORS